ON RELATIONSHIPS

An Anthology

FOREWORD

Why relationships? It's a word that embodies every interaction we have with other people And yet is incredibly difficult to pin down how they have shaped us, how they make us who we are.

In the past year, a lot has changed for me personally and politically. I've lost someone I loved and changed jobs to a much smaller company. What I've learnt is how powerful my friendships have been in protecting me, in powering me. Two weeks ago, the Labour Party lost to the Conservatives and Boris Johnson. Boris Johnson is not someone who values relationships. His cynical ascent to power has depressed me, to say the least. Online and offline, it feels like everyone is fighting, everyone is angry and looking for someone to blame. We are facing very hard times ahead.

But there is something else happening. People knocked tirelessly on doors, people have been raising money for the homeless, the disabled, the NHS and so much more. Money for people they've never met, or interacted with. What I've learnt is that humans can only survive with the help of others.

And it's not always financial. Our friends and family shape us, they challenge us, and they love us. Not to get too *Love Actually* on you, but the past year has taught me that our most important relationships are ones of love and respect.

I hope you have great relationships in your lives. 3 of Cups has brought me some of my best ones, and I sincerely believe that art is often the way to love.

Clare Bogen, December 2019

Published in 2019 by
3 of Cups Press
London

Paperback ISBN 9781999877668

Printed and bound by CPI Group (UK) Ltd,
Croydon, CR0 4YY

Cover design by Harriet Smelt & Clare Bogen

www.3ofcups.co.uk

Contents

FOREWORD   II

FAMILY MAGIC
Lauren Vevers   1

SUNDAY SERVICE
Melissa Gitari   9

WHAT BECOMES OF
THE CRAZY RICH ASIAN?
Rebecca Liu   21

TWO POEMS
Susannah Dickey   29

THE WAY
Vanessa Pelz-Sharpe   33

IN BIRTH
Tori Truslow   39

BRAID MY HAIR
Zahrah Nesbitt-Ahmed   49

COMMUNITY
Marian Sloane   63

OLIVE BRANCH
Maz Hedgehog   67

DINNER, AT THE TABLE
Lexi Earl   69

CAMBRIC
Mikael Johani   73

BILANG DENGAN BUNGA
Anya Rompas   83

FIRM GROUND
Kasim Mohammed   87

MIRACLE
Jen Calleja   107

LOVE
Isha Karki   121

HOW TO WIN AT THE GAME OF LIFE
Kate Young   133

MADE VISIBLE BY DISTANCE
Anna Kahn   143

OVER
So Mayer   152

RESOURCES
                                                  161

AUTHOR BIOS
                                                  167

FAMILY MAGIC

Lauren Vevers

I come from a line of witches, from women who perform rituals to keep themselves and their loved ones safe. Her name was Elizabeth although everyone called her Nancy. I learned to talk at a young age but couldn't fit my mouth around the *nuh* sound so I called her an approximation of her name, Minty. It caught on in our immediate family and that's how I knew her. Each year, I'd receive birthday and Christmas cards signed in big, flamboyant handwriting: *lots of love Grandma Minty and Roy*. Roy, her dog. Together they lived in a tiny two-bed terrace where my mam and her sister grew up; where my mam's dad and stepdad died; where her half-brother lives now. Nothing about Grandma Minty's life was particularly extravagant although there were a handful of exceptions.

She had a passionate love for cream cakes of all kinds: peach melba, custard slice and black forest gateau. For pudding, she'd have an eclair with a strawberry tart on the side. Lashings of pouring cream on top, always. To finish she'd eat jelly sweets; giant sticky opals coated in beads of crystallised sugar. Then liquorice bullets; digestive letters posted one after the other in the car on the way home. If she had her way she'd forget about her main course in favour of the sweet treats she knew lay waiting. And who could blame her? Dessert was the best bit.

1

She rarely wore make-up. In that way, Grandma Minty wasn't glamorous. She kept her hair in a functional grey crop. I remember her in knee-length skirts and orthopaedic shoes and tan-coloured pop socks. In winter, though, she adorned fabulous coats that were enveloping and regal. She wore them with costume jewellery, gaudy brooches in the shape of animals and flowers. She had long nails, unmanicured, which clacked on the piano keys when she played. The piano was the only true luxury item in her house. Almost everything else was functional or kept for best.

***

My hands are like my mam's with plump palms and a little finger that turns inwards at the end. I'm fine-tuned to the detail because in this moment I'm certain she is about to die. Now there's nothing left to say but *I love you* which I say until the words lose all meaning. I want to keep saying them in case these are the last words I say to her. It's hopeless trying to condense years of complicated feeling into coherent sentences. For all of us the end is inevitable yet somehow it's still a shock when the threat of it arrives in our lives, a thunderbolt out of the dark. I've been here with my mam before and I thought I'd be more prepared. But in the face of death language falls short. So I say *I love you* until the syllables merge into one. We gather her things. The crash team explain that she will be taken up to the Intensive Care Unit. When I'm alone I say *I love you* again, softly and to myself, like a spell.

***

Grandma Minty was superstitious. She was brought up by her grandparents who were old-fashioned and strict. For her, the world was a scary place. She could feel danger lurking around every corner. You were never to wear green, as it would guarantee bad luck. Salt should be thrown over the left shoulder into the eye of the devil. If shoes were placed on a table, it was thought to tempt ill-fate. These were the rules Mam lived by too. They were supposed to keep everyone safe.

Superstition can be a belief in magic or a reverence to the supernatural. In my family, to live superstitiously is also to live in anticipation of the very worst. For both Grandma Minty and my mam, their fears were compounded by death and uncertainty; they imagined awful things and often those things happened. In their working-class community, stoicism and the ability to keep going were valued above everything else. This was a burden suffered by everyone and especially by the women, whose duty it was to care and to nurture and to hold the fragility of life in their hands until it was fragile no more.

**

It's a week after Mam is taken into hospital, and I'm finding it difficult to walk out my front door. The outside world is too volatile. Small fears become big fears with no difference between them. A friend lends me Ariel Levy's *The Rules Do Not Apply* which I read greedily. It feels like a gift. I race through it chapter by chapter until I have to stop, floored by her description *grief is a world we walk through, unshelled and unskinned.*[1]

That afternoon I obsessively tidy the kitchen. I organise the tupperware in size-order. I stack tin by tin by tin as if it will somehow make things better. Once the cupboards are arranged, my anxiety is temporarily quelled and I'm back in control. I return to the book. Levy writes of her miscarriage

and I knew, as surely as I now knew that I wanted a child, that this change in fortune was my fault. I had boarded a plane out of vanity and selfishness, and the dark Mongolian sky had punished me. I was still a witch but my powers were all gone.[2]

As I read I think about Mam and about a story I've heard in fragments. Grandma Minty went into early labour. My mam is only twelve but she knows; the baby is coming. She calls for help but they're alone; there is no time for painkillers or the hospital. Her little brother is born right there on the living room floor, breech, the umbilical cord wrapped around his neck. Terrified, she speaks to God as she watches his gossamer skin turn blue. Against all natural odds, he survives. That night my mam goes to bed convinced her prayers have kept him safe. Since that day she has said prayers to protect us all.

I clean some more. I can't bring myself to pray.

***

1 Ariel Levy, *The Rules Do Not Apply*, ed. 2019 Random House p. 158
2 ibid p. 147

For stretches of time Grandma Minty won't leave the house. This is mentioned to me in passing as a child. We generally don't talk about mental illness; if we do it's through gentle euphemisms. *She's not quite herself.* So when I hear *agoraphobia* it sounds harsh, unusually clinical. It's explained to me kindly and simply that Grandma Minty is sometimes afraid of being outside. Only as an adult can I fully comprehend the severity of the situation. I think about how lonely she must've felt and how Minty's agoraphobia impacted my mam because she had to assume too much responsibility before she was fully grown.

Care-giving is a script that women in my family follow diligently. Growing up, Mam was surrounded by death. Grandma Minty volunteered to nurse sick relatives. She took them into her home to help them find peace and pass with dignity. Her kindness was all-encompassing but it took its toll. When there is no limit to how much you will give, you are mostly left with nothing. It was hard for Mam too; she was fenced in by the darkness all around her.

***

I order groceries online even though the supermarket is less than half a mile away and I can't justify the minimum spend for delivery. I get out of bed so I can go to the hospital at visiting hours. I call a taxi because the last time I was on public transport I had a panic attack. I don't reply to texts from friends. I'm clouded by mental fog and spiralling thoughts that drag the worst parts of the past round and round my brain until all I can do is lie down in the dark. I have deadlines. I'm meant to be working, writing. My body won't let me; it's as though I'm carrying three generations' worth of pain.

Mam's behaviour as a mother echoed the example she was set. From the beginning I was taught about the violent unpredictability of things. I was taught that to overcome fear you should imagine every variable, every consequence; that you should build walls around yourself; that you should prepare for endless possibilities through meticulous planning. But you can't think away sudden illness or heartbreak or bad luck before it's upon you. That isn't the way the universe works. And as much as it's comforting to believe in magic and to believe that our personal magic has the ability to wield power over our own fate, it's also an exhausting way to live. It's hardly like living at all.

***

The day Grandma Minty dies, I arrive home from school to find Mam sitting on the front steps. I'm only twelve but I know. She would later tell me that there is no greater loss than the loss of a mother – it's an absence that forever stings. In the years after, my mam performs tiny rituals in tribute. She picks up bags of jelly sweets and places them thoughtfully back on the shelf. She keeps a sentimental bar of Yardley Lavender soap, wrapped in floral paper, at the back of her dresser drawer. When shopping she stops in the dessert aisle with her hand hovering over the strawberry tarts. If I'm with her, we look on together. We pause in reverence at the rows of pastries and cream cakes in their plastic boxes, wordlessly united in our grief as the world continues to turn around us.

* * *

Mam is calling via FaceTime. When the video is live, I can just see her eyebrows. She's finally home from the hospital after being discharged. The emergency surgery they performed saved her life although her health complications continue. Dad floats into the background to help her adjust the camera. I can hear the whistle of the kettle and electronic whir of her motorised wheelchair. She's telling me about a good deal she's seen on the shopping channel. Everything is back to a version of normal. I'm grateful to be able to have these everyday conversations with her; they're suddenly very precious. After we hang up my natural instinct is to clean, to stay inside, to hide away; anything to restore order to the chaos of my spiralling thoughts. I'm worried that any small change might encourage a cruel twist of fate. But I resist the urge to wear the same coat for a week just in case. I don't throw salt over my left shoulder or avoid the colour green. I continue to practise our family magic on my own terms; I'm learning to stare down an unknowable future and to sit quietly with fear until it starts to feel something like hope.

SUNDAY SERVICE

Melissa Gitari

It starts with the clash of cymbals.

The nervous teen on the drums has come in too early but is swiftly overshadowed by the dreadlocked pianist, whose practised fingers glide across the keys. Their efforts are an accompaniment to this morning's main event: the choir.

The noise the choir makes is astounding, and not just because Pastor insisted on spending £5,000 on surround-sound speakers last year. These women infuse the hymns with their own personal sorrows. Afua, a nurse at the struggling hospital on the outskirts of town, wails the lyrics of 'How Great Is Our God' as she thinks about the shift she has to rush to as soon as service is over. Elderly Edna warbles with eyes closed and right hand raised, taking pause every few lines to cough into her handkerchief. They were chosen not for their vocal talent, but for proving themselves to be Devout African Matriarchs. This is a woman for whom the church is an extension of herself, a child she must micromanage into perfection.

You can recognise them by their clothing. Elegant brocade dresses that seem more appropriate for a red carpet than for hours of praise and worship. During the designated prayer time that is supposed to be silent but never is, you can hear sequins scraping and costume jewels jangling as the wearer shifts in her seat. Some of the women wrap their geles so tightly around their heads that their pencilled-in eyebrows take on an even more exaggerated arch.

Eunice, one of the choir's newest recruits, is dazzling today in a floor-length mermaid gown that accentuates what Pastor calls (privately, of course) her God-given assets. She keeps her eyes glued to her lyric book – she knows Pastor is watching her from his lectern. If you were unfortunate enough to be a single woman under forty attending Victory in Christ Pentecostal Church, you learned to avoid being alone with Pastor at all costs for his hands tended to wander. It is not his fault, some of the older women say. His wife died two years ago and he's very lonely. You'd think with all the pastorly business keeping him busy, he wouldn't have time for trifling matters of the flesh. To this, elderly Edna would shrug and wheeze, 'A man is a man is a man.'

The loudest among the choir singers is Joy, whose mother warned her as a child that if she did not lift her voice in praise then God would not know she loved Him and she would surely go to Hell. She loves being in the choir, looking out at the congregation and witnessing the Holy Spirit at work. From her vantage point, Joy spies her friend Beatrice deep in prayer, eyes clenched and body trembling with the force of her reverence. Apart from a few disgruntled teenagers, everyone is on their feet, some even dancing in the aisles. She likes to think that it is her voice, one of God's favourite instruments, that invigorates the congregation so.

Her husband Robert stands fidgeting in one of the middle rows, the waistband of his ill-fitting trousers constricting his stomach. Robert isn't particularly religious – he'd spent the majority of his forty-eight years wondering what kind of God would leave him and his brother orphaned as children and at the mercy of their wicked uncle. Uncle Peter would beat them until brown skin turned purple simply because they were there, another expense draining his already dwindling resources.

Robert came to church only for Joy, coerced by that unspoken marital law that forces spouses into doing things they hate for their other half. And yet, some part of him hoped that one Sunday he'd be struck by the Divine, and the collection of personal misfortunes he'd accrued over his lifetime would become easier to carry. Standing there now, though, mouthing along to whatever the congregation is shrieking, Robert struggles to imagine how he will ever find solace amid this spectacle.

* * *

The room smells like sweat and crisp banknotes. There is no clock in the church and the only windows are sealed tight and hidden behind navy velvet curtains. No room in here for the outside world and its multitude of sins. The church transcends the rules of time so that a four-hour service seems to stretch on for eternity, as if it can only end when God Himself comes down to cast judgement on his earthly children.

At the front of the church, beside the pastor's podium, is a large marble vase about the size of a small child. One by one the congregation flock to this vessel, waving their white envelopes to deposit in its gaping mouth. The act of giving is an intricate performance that can take up to half an hour. They move as one very long Very Hungry Caterpillar made of bright, clashing fabrics.

Melissa Gitari

At last, the singing stops, and the choir make their way to their seats in the front row. Pastor dabs his perspiring forehead with a wad of kitchen towel before adjusting the microphone on his lectern.

'The Lord is good,' he growls.
'All the time!' The church wails in agreement.
'And all the time?'
'The Lord is good!'

This back and forth continues for about thirty seconds, until the pastor, satisfied, resumes his sermon. Today's address follows the same formula as any other: a rumination on a current social malady (this morning it is People Who Worship False Idols, Like Reality TV Stars) followed by some lengthy scripture readings and, of course, ousting Satan and all his companions with the power of song.

The service comes to a close and the building lets out a sigh of relief. Time for food. There is a mass exodus to the refreshments table at the back of the massive hall.

Joy and some of her choirmates stand by the table of treats, sipping tea and discussing churchly matters.

'Have you heard about Anthea?' Betty whispers.

'Ghanaian Anthea or Sierra Leonian Anthea?' Joy asks.

'The Ghanaian one, oh!' Betty yelps, her bulbous eyes scanning the room to make sure the Anthea in question is not within earshot. She is not. Betty continues.

'Let's just say it's not only her husband keeping her bed warm at night.'

'It's a lie!' Eunice gasps, clutching her gold necklace.

'May God strike me down if it is so,' says Betty, making

12

the sign of the cross.

A few feet away, Robert is pretending to listen to a young man's story of how he became born again while eyeing the plate of meat pies on the refreshments table. He stands there nodding complacently for half an hour until his wife, finished with her socialising, informs him that it is time to leave. By now, the meat pies are all gone.

***

Joy and Robert returned to their cluttered, tiny home in silence. Although they'd tried to make the place look homely with overpriced wall carvings from Nairobi and kente-patterned throw pillows, the squalor poked through like a pimple. The coffee table was patterned with sticky brown crescent moons, and a large pile of unfolded laundry lay insolently on the sofa. The room smelled like mothballs and the fried eggs they'd had for breakfast. Joy dropped her handbag on the floor, unwrapped her gele and made towards her favourite armchair when she tripped on one of Robert's work boots.

'What have I told you about leaving your rubbish lying around?' She picked up the boot and threw it at her husband, whose reflexes were too slow to dodge.

'Maybe if your one hundred pairs of shoes weren't clogging the storage cupboard I'd have somewhere to keep my own,' Robert muttered, rubbing his sore arm.

'Continue mumbling-mumbling to yourself and see what happens,' Joy retorted, taking off her cropped black wig and garish earrings.

Robert rolled his eyes and made for the kitchen. Pre-empting his next move, Joy was quick at his heels like a hunting dog.

'What do you think you're doing?' Joy snapped. Robert had opened the fridge and taken out a container of beef stew.

'See I'm eating lunch. What's the problem?'

'You want to finish the meat that I went all the way to West Green Road to buy and then spent two hours cooking while you sat on the sofa salivating like a dog? Heh!'

She clapped her hands. 'Today, you and I will fight, Robert Odinga!'

'Ah, Joy! Why are you always trying to quarrel?'

'And why are you so useless? I work forty hours a week, cook, clean, everything. Meanwhile, you can't even wash your own pants and you are still a factory hand at the age of forty-eight. You know, today at church I caught up with Celestine. Do you remember her? The Congolese woman who bleaches too much?'

'I don't—'

'Her husband was recently promoted to manager at his bank. Celestine says they can now afford to send their children to private school. Imagine. Whenever people ask me about my own husband I have nothing to say. Sometimes I think it would be better if I were a widow.'

'Joy, if you continue disrespecting me in my own house I'll—'

'Heh! You'll what?' Joy's eyes widened in mock-disbelief. 'What will you do? What have you ever done in your miserable little life? You couldn't even give me one single child. God, what did I do to deserve this man?' Joy raised her eyes.

Robert stormed out of the room, leaving Joy to help herself to the stew.

***

It would be comforting to say that she hadn't always been like this, that some traumatic experience had filled this once sweet girl with venom and thorns. But even as a child, Joy revelled in using whatever means necessary to get her way. She figured that she could do whatever she wanted as long as she said a really long prayer afterwards. After all, did God not sacrifice His only son to wash away her sins? At least, that's how Joy justified stealing the largest piece of meat from her mother's pot of stew and blaming it on her unassuming younger sister, who took a hefty beating for Joy's gluttony. To Joy religion was malleable, a block of plasticine to be moulded into whatever she wanted it to be.

Sometimes, as in the case of Robert and Joy, the universe throws two people together, not because they are meant to be, but because no-one else will have them.

They met at Kenya University. It was her final year and Joy had still never had a boyfriend. All of her friends were planning weddings or moving in with their partners while she grew more surly and unapproachable as graduation inched closer. You see, Joy is not a beautiful woman. She has plain, no-nonsense eyes that do not sparkle. Eyes that exist purely for the purpose of seeing. She has always been short and stout like a sack of rice. And yet, there is an openness to her face that makes people endear to her. The creases on her face seem to denote every emotion she's ever felt, each wince of pain, each peal of laughter.

When Robert first saw Joy frowning at her notes in the library, he was drawn to this face. Not in a sexual way as such, but in a sympathetic one. Here is a woman that has suffered but refuses to be broken by her suffering. He had the same feeling months later when he decided he wanted to propose to her. They were sitting at a grimy plastic table in front of a stand selling *nyama choma* on the roadside. Joy was ripping into a piece of charred meat, brow furrowed in concentration. She always ate like she didn't know where her next meal was coming from. Robert loved how she wasn't afraid to look ugly, how she wasn't constantly wiping the grease off her face. Joy didn't even bother to use toothpicks, preferring to save the morsels of meat in her teeth for later.

And so, the spindly engineering postgrad plucked up the courage to ask the grumpy woman with sensibly cornrowed hair to marry him. To Joy, he was neither physically attractive nor a compelling conversationalist, but he tolerated her incessant evangelising and was also rumoured to be moving to London after completing his studies. She'd always wanted to live in the UK. With an engineering degree, Robert was sure to get a good job and buy her a house with a marble staircase. She'd seen one in a Spanish soap opera and decided that possessing one was the definitive marker of success.

***

When Joy walked into the sitting room carrying a plate of reheated rice and stew, she found her husband sitting on top of the clothes on the sofa with a haunted look on his face.

'Can you get your fat behind off my work clothes!' She placed her food on the coffee table and shooed Robert away with an old *Evening Standard*.

'Do you know what today is?' Robert said.

'It will be the day you are struck dead if you don't get off my clean laundry!'

'It's... it's been ten years since the... car accident.'

'The what? Ah, you're still upset about that? I told you if you pray well, God will forgive you.'

'I can't believe it's been ten years already.'

Joy had lost interest in this conversation. She parked herself in the armchair and began assaulting her food.

Robert turned to her. 'I should have ignored you and gone to the police. God, what was I thinking?'

'I'm telling you, me I've read the Bible,' said Joy through a mouthful of food. 'In this situation, the only thing to do is pray for God's forgiveness. What happened happened. What would confessing have done? Would it have brought that person back?'

Robert loosened his tie and let out a weary breath.

'Maybe I'll go to Kenya for a bit, clear my head.'

'My friend, you're not going anywhere,' Joy scoffed. 'With what money will you buy a plane ticket?'

Robert could only hear fragments of the words his wife spoke. 'You're right, running away won't solve this problem. This guilt has been gnawing at me for a decade. I must hand myself into the police. I must confess.' Robert stared into the middle distance like he was speaking in a trance. With that, he stood up as fast as his creaky knees would let him and made for the front door.

'Are you mad? If you confess everyone will know I married a killer, a spineless man who ran over a boy and left him bleeding to death in the street!'

***

The weary drunk driver takes his eyes off the road for just one second.

When he gets home, the drunk driver's wife is doubly furious – at being woken up in the middle of the night, and at having to now calm her hyperventilating husband. She slaps him twice, tells him to go to the car wash and never breathe a word of this to anyone.

A few days later, the drunk driver stares into the teary eyes of the victim's mother through the TV. She pleads with him to share any information he has, anything that will get the monster who killed her son put behind bars. The drunk driver's wife sits in her armchair, praying aloud for Jesus to prevent any policemen from coming to her home and throwing her husband in jail, for how would she be able to show her face in church again?

* * *

'I need to face what I did.' Robert opened the door and stepped out onto a street of crumbling terraced houses. The houses on Wormwood Road were painted in various pastel shades but were uniform in their decrepitude. Robert hated this street. Terraced housing made him feel claustrophobic; the walls were so thin that he could hear every intimate sound from the houses on either side. And yet, despite this proximity, the residents of Wormwood Road lived isolated lives. It was so alien to him that neighbours didn't greet each other every day or even make eye contact. He longed for Kenya, for the loving home he lived in before his parents died. Standing in his driveway, Robert realised that after what he was about to do, he might never see Kenya again. Nevertheless, he walked on.

At the sight of her husband's receding silhouette, Joy began to panic. She put her wig on with haste and stuffed her feet into her house slippers.

'Robert, stop being stupid. Come back now!'

Her eyes scanned the street to make sure no-one was watching them. She didn't want to give those haughty whites the satisfaction of seeing two Africans making a scene.

By now, Robert was behind the wheel of his battered Ford Fiesta. Before he could put the key in the ignition, Joy was in front of the car, arms folded over her matronly bosom.

'You'd better run me over because turning yourself in and making me the subject of idle gossip is as good as killing me anyway,' Joy said, with the vitriol of a Nollywood actress.

Unfortunately, Robert had already turned the ignition and did not catch his wife's stellar performance. He started reversing.

In a last-ditch attempt, Joy threw herself on the bonnet. It was the closest thing to an embrace that the two had shared in years. They locked eyes for a bit, hers dark and stony, his slightly jaundiced, and neither of them expected him to leave. Then something, not the Divine but something similar, made Robert honk his horn which startled Joy off the car and allowed him to drive away.

Joy watched the tail lights speed off in disbelief. For a moment, her face crumpled as if she was about to cry but she remembered herself, adjusted her wig and walked back into her house.

WHAT BECOMES OF THE
CRAZY RICH ASIAN?

Rebecca Liu

Ultra Rich Asian Girls of Vancouver premiered on YouTube in October 2014 under the purview of Canadian entertainment company 'Hot Bitches in Charge TV'. The brainchild of Chinese-Canadian television mogul Kevin K. Li, the reality television series tracked the lives of young women who formed part of Vancouver's second wave of immigrants from East Asia: a new monied class who seemed strikingly different from their relatively modest first-wave counterparts. Positioned in the vein of *Real Housewives*-style insider television, in which elite lives are both vaunted and debased through the camera's all-seeing eye, the programme showcased four fashionable young women who spent their days, in Li's words, 'having fun, spending daddy's money... enjoying life and funding an economy'.[1] The opening scene of the show sees the cast, beautiful well-dressed twenty-something women from China and Taiwan, enjoying a light meal at Vancouver's luxury Black & Blue steakhouse. The leader

---

1 Quoted in Ian Young's 'Nose Jobs, Champagne and Lamborghinis: A Hot Mess of "Ultra-Rich Asians" in Vancouver', *South China Morning Post*, 11 June 2014.

of the pack, twenty-four--year-old Chelsea Jiang, authoritatively orders a glass of wine – the 1995 Château Latour, currently on sale at Cult Wines for £525[2] – before requesting a straw. 'You don't want to stain your teeth,' she explains to her new social rivals.

A straw may not have been the most environmentally friendly choice, but then again it was 2014, before many of us came to recognise our reliance on extraneous plastics. A lot has happened since then. The percolating interest in wealthy East Asians has since exploded into a global cultural phenomenon. Social media is full of jokes about impossibly stylish international students, seemingly coded as East Asian, who show up to early morning lectures dressed in the latest Louis Vuitton to the shame of their slovenly Western peers. Facing a spate of incoming wealth from Asia, governments across Canada, Australia and New Zealand have enacted laws curbing foreign purchases of real estate. This explosive growth is seen in its extreme in modern-day China, which – in barely fifty years – has grown from an agrarian war-torn society to become one of the world's leading economic superpowers. Now, the ascendant wealthy have come to collect their riches, commanding scandalous headline after scandalous headline. The son of China's richest man outraged a nation when he shared pictures of his dog wearing two gold Apple watches on social media. A new 'Flaunt Your Wealth' meme among the new Chinese *fuerdai*[3] (a term for the children of the nouveau riche) has young

2   https://www.wineinvestment.com/wine/bordeaux/pauillac/chateau-latour/latour/1995/. Price as of 16 August 2019.
3   https://www.bloomberg.com/news/features/2015-10-01/children-of-the-yuan-percent-everyone-hates-china-s-rich-kids

heirs and heiresses pretending to 'fall' out of cars, dropping luxury items in their wake. A young woman in a red dress is seen face-down on a concrete slab, her Louboutin-clad foot elegantly perched on top of her black Mercedes-Benz. Her reposing body is surrounded by a carefully placed melange of Chanel bags and purses.

***

Hollywood has noticed. When *Crazy Rich Asians* was released in the summer of 2018, it came loaded with a host of political expectations that seemed out of step with the film's actual status as a feel-good Hollywood romcom. The excitement was understandable given it was the first Hollywood film with an all-Asian cast in twenty-five years. The blockbuster featured a host of East Asian entertainers across the diaspora: American *Fresh Off the Boat* sitcom queen Constance Wu, Malaysian television presenter Henry Golding, seasoned British actress Gemma Chan, New-York-rapper-turned-actress Awkwafina, Australian-Malaysian comedian Ronny Chieng, among others. Set in modern-day Singapore, the film lingered over the island's beatific street food markets, glitzy high-rise buildings, and tucked-away stately homes. Wealthy wives hid designer purchases from their moderately less wealthy husbands. Unruly bachelors flew in models from abroad to attend blowout boat parties. Opulent family parties were hosted, less in the interest of celebrating the ones they loved and more to show off to the ones they didn't. Household servants, often South Asian, linger around the edges of the film, which eschews an ethical excavation of what this tiered social life means to instead focus on the 1% travails of their ethnically Chinese employers. Billed as a simple American-girl-meets-boy story but with a twist (boy, the girl discovers, is actually an extremely rich heir to a Singaporean business dynasty and a nationally sought-after bachelor), *Crazy Rich Asians* opted for happiness over pathos; celebration over reckoning. Mild conflicts were ultimately pasted over by a picture-perfect Hollywood ending; our lovebirds fought, briefly broke up, and then finally reunited, engagement ring in tow. The film wanted to be beautiful, which was its way of grappling with its underlying politics. It was, after all, a light-hearted storyline that wasn't interested in addressing political questions in the first place. When you become vested with the burden of long-overdue representation, an easy response is to make everyone preternaturally beautiful, and the world they inhabit superficially gorgeous too.

The underlying tension of *Crazy Rich Asians* centres around Eleanor Young, a queenly mother figure played by Michelle Yeoh, who is struggling with her ever-unravelling grip on her son's life. Her son Nick has been living in New York; a temporary stay, she hopes. When he arrives back in Singapore with a new American girlfriend, Eleanor realises that her precious plans for her son – to move him back to Singapore, and put him in charge of the family business – are falling apart. A battle for Nick's soul then ensues between Eleanor and Rachel, Nick's girlfriend played by Constance Wu. An older, monied Singaporean woman faces off with a younger working-class New York immigrant. Because this is Hollywood, Rachel wins. Because this is Hollywood, she wins politely, even prematurely conceding defeat in a high-stakes mahjong game against Eleanor – the good American of our Hollywood screens, always winning precisely because they didn't want to. Because this is Hollywood, we learn that it is Eleanor Young who needs to adapt to the modern world, her neo-Confucian love of the family a mere relic in this new, energetic world that celebrates individual dreams. All underlying conflicts of the film are then resolved, swallowed whole by the all-encompassing power of love. Or so we think. For a romantic comedy, it seems strange that the sought-after bachelor of *Crazy Rich Asians* is ultimately a bland, blank slate with nothing much to say about the civilisational struggles between his girlfriend and his mother, despite having a foot in both worlds. In the end, the true love story of *Crazy Rich Asians* is the classic Hollywood infatuation with the idea of wholesale self-invention that batters past all real-world structural constraints. There is much more heart, spirit and sexual excitement in the film's makeover scene, which sees Rachel breathlessly trying on designer gowns far beyond anything she can afford – a glitzy Michael Kors number, an artsy Dior gown – than in any interaction between the leading couple. We can all, with the right amount of money and unfettered access to lavish goods, *be beautiful*.

As the film draws to a close aboard a – where else? – gargantuan 'surfboard-like' rooftop structure that adjoins three gigantic skyscrapers, Eleanor gives Rachel a brief, gentle nod, and we are made to believe that all ends have been tied up. The temporarily separated couple are now reunited and happily engaged. The couple are free to enjoy their gorgeous, unencumbered lives together. But as we see Rachel and Nick embrace, it is Michelle Yeoh's ambivalent, hardened eyes that I think of, and the enduring story of Eleanor Young. She has everything in the world except the thing she cares about the most. What does it mean to lose something you have held so dear, to move in a world that has rewarded you so lavishly but at this price?

***

Money can buy many things, even respect. In *Crazy Rich Asians*, wealthy Singaporeans flaunt Western signifiers, endlessly one-upping each other in the game of cultural capital. Your child goes to boarding school in England. You might even be briefly featured in American *Vogue*. Your wardrobe is filled with French designers – you could even have a second home in Paris. Though much is made of how the East Asian 1% will displace their Western counterparts, lost in these narratives is how intimately and inextricably the ego of this emergent class is endlessly tied up with the ghosts of 'sophisticated' 'Western modernity'.

But there are limits. As Eleanor Young learns, money can't fully buy away the shadow of colonial-era insecurities, or get you back your culturally Westernised children. These depictions of the East Asian elite, so often outwardly glazed in a forward-looking triumphalism, are submerged in an understated loss and melancholia. There is one version of *Crazy Rich Asians*: the campy, celebratory romcom dipped in thoroughly American cultural sensibilities, which encourages you to cheer for the happy couple and all the gorgeous friends and unfettered wealth they will have in their new lives. There is also another: the story of the confused, last gasp of a tiny, privileged slice of a culture collapsing under the weight of its own ambitions. With her son gone, who, or what, does Eleanor Young have left? With all her wealth, she was allowed to participate in the relentless march to Western capitalist modernity that has left so many behind; but in the end, where does this project lead you, beyond rendering you irrelevant? Here, *Crazy Rich Asians*, as specific as it is to a tiny slice of culture, offers a lesson with a universal resonance: global capitalism, far from being an abstract financial force, seeps into our everyday relationships. Sometimes, it breaks them.

TWO POEMS

Susannah Dickey

South Bank can get so hot in May
and a young woman is falling apart

I buy a cheesecake in the café of a concert hall there are three
layers to it it goes brown then dark yellow then light yellow.
The rumoured summer has come. There are tits

on display and it's horrible and it's lovely and there are
people on this fake beach writing love messages in the sand.
The graphic of a v-shaped heart between two initials

makes a relationship into a court proceeding. Across the big
grey slabs of the veranda there's a woman turning to ash
on a plastic chair. Her ears and shoulders are dandruffing off

rude as confessions and all over her skin skate parks are being
carved out. [Her teeth eroded limestone her mouth sings
like a tuning fork.] By the time this scraped-empty

cheesecake tub makes its discarded way to the bin to the sewers
to the chalky river to the manmade shore the woman will
have disappeared and probably R and K or S and S won't be

together anymore. It's so easy to ignore things when it's like
this a cry for help is green-tinged gum on the pavement
when it's like this. A breeze will carry her off soon. Nothing
    left

but her jeans and her knickers and her sandals what might
    seem
like a big event to a small life needn't be all that big. She'll be
gone soon and that's alright she'll be mistaken for detritus

dropped bits of old cheesecake and that's alright. I think D
and T will make it you know. They always were the best of us.
The Thames moves like dialysis. In this light everyone

looks beautiful.

a black cloth over your face is not the same as night

I spent the summer controlling two people in a video game.
I made him tall and handsome and a piano teacher I made her
patent the peanut-size sheath that keeps umbrellas open

that keeps them from collapse. She got picked up for work
in a mint green Datsun every morning. One day I made him
drop a wallet in the street I made her ding ding hurtle

after him like a sneeze. I watched their nail-less fingers
touch and then I intervened because god [!]
think of a pursuit less fruitful than affinity. I made them go

about their days so he married a dentist and she died
young and he used up his days evading
diagnoses of bruxism and she died young neither was

handed the sticky debasement of a life spent
wanting. Their lives were lilac there was no asbestos slung
behind their walls. The destiny we might want is not

what we are necessarily owed you know? Autumn is here
and I need a life soft-edged with a heart motif, a little girl's ring
bound notebook. I need insight and it oozes from the corners

like navy damp ding ding you are a product of your choices
you are a totem pole you are hunger on top of caprice on top
of the grazed cheeks of your nights spent folded face

in the gravel like an animal. I decide to fix things I apply
streamlined practices I wear a yellow mini dress in an always
temperate clime. My house is pristine now and if it's not I'll just

eat [or fuck or swim] to lessen the scores of it all. I'll buy a
  dog
and I'll teach the dog to die and when it does my kids will be
prepared for everything in the world. Finally when my life

is panacea smooth a new person will enter the game
ding ding yes it is attainment. We'll dance together.
We'll dance to the open fire on the stovetop to the graceless

wordless music to the all the things I mistook
for the sky. We'll dance to the entombed cockatoo moans
of my dog buried neatly beneath the geranium bush.

THE WAY

Vanessa Pelz-Sharpe

On the hill outside my childhood home I want to thrust my hands into the soil, push them down like trowels, up to my wrists. We lived here for fourteen years, the longest time I have lived anywhere in fact. In my memory I can walk the single hallway that our flat was built around and describe everything, from the colours of each skirting board to the glow in the dark stars on my bedroom ceiling. The soil is chocolate cake wet, the toes of my shoes forming little dents. This hill isn't really a hill, it's a slope. A thick grass verge with a brown-grey brick wall at the bottom and blocks of grey concrete flats at the top. Before that it was nothing. Grass, fields, hay. We used to make hay in Edgware, thrown on the back of carts and plodded into London proper. They took the same route we do now: a straight line down a long incline. Down through Colindale, Hendon, down down through the north-west edge of the city. No directions needed, just keep going and you're there. Track back, before the hay and the fields and no-one knows. There was a village with a church and a school so someone must have lived here. There was a manor house where Handel composed in leisure. Until the family lost all their money and the building was taken apart piece by piece. The columns were dragged ten miles to form the portico of the National Gallery. The rest went here, there. In my mind I see carts travelling up and down the road following the ancient trackway as though by habit.

We have always been poor in Edgware. The manor house was a blip. A moment when Edgware was rich and fashionable, and people came up from the city to walk the grounds and ogle the most expensive house in the country. But when it went the land was ours again. Ours as in the people who have moved through Edgware. Because it has always been a place you don't stay. The trackway led people from the sea, through the cities, and up out to the wide plains of the countryside. It threaded between villages, never quite reaching them, as it left the south-east: some say we have our directions wrong, since who would have wanted to have walked so close but yet so far from humans and habitation? Though when I am back in Edgware I don't look up my old school friends, or buzz any of my old neighbours; I want to glide from my childhood home, along the journeys I made time and time again. Sometimes I take my bike and cycle from home to my old school then back. Cross the A5 over and over again towards the old cinema, now flats, towards the old library, now also flats. There is a man on Yelp who describes this place as a 'shithole'. They're reviewing B&K Salt Beef Bar & Restaurant, a place of absolute mystery during my goyish vegetarian childhood. Now an omnivore, I know that behind the brown smoked glass windows there lies wood panelling and a lino floor. That inside there is rye and thin pink slivers of salt beef. As I step out of B&K onto the road I think about that review. Taking a bite I look at the junction, the old churchyard, the empty office tower in the distance. It feels like home. It's my shithole.

When the underground arrived in Edgware it was still a village. My primary school existed, and the church, a short row of shops, then open fields on every side. As London grew, people were encouraged to take the sprawl of their lives outwards and move into the suburbs. They were promised everything you dream of when staring out a grimy attic window. Gardens, allotments, clean fresh crisp air to fill your lungs with. Slum clearances swept the inner city, hastened by German bombs, and soon entire communities were flowing northwards. The do-wells built flat low houses on the edge of the green belt. Dozens upon dozens of identical homes sometimes in semicircles but others following the earth. Snaking across ridges with garden lawns that dove downhill. On the southern side of town we found ourselves pressed up against the old road. We clustered together like bugs, living against, on top of, cheek to cheek with each other. Though we had tried to escape the slums, out here amongst the fields we missed them. Each morning we flooded to the station and back into the city. There were houses now, a few shops, some pubs, but still we were city people. We had not let go. We weren't staying in Edgware, not for long anyway.

Edgware takes its name from Ecgi, a Saxon man, with a pond or *weir*. My dad refused to believe this was true: no-one would ever name a place after something as boring as some random man's fishing pond. I think of Ecgi and his weir often. We people who made Edgware are nothing special. Edgware never made the decision to become a place. No-one ever turned up with graph paper and a plan to rearrange this blank grass landscape. The way I think about it, we were always here.

Before my mother came from Italy, before my dad moved down from Yorkshire. Before the Cockneys wandered out of the slums. Before the tube and the tram and the train. Before the church and Handel and the Doric arches. Before Romans paved it, before even Ecgi and his weir. Before all of that was the soil and I want to put my hands in it. On that sticky thick London clay people walked, argued, fucked, died. Their footsteps made the backbone of our town, an ancient trackway, around which we still gather.

Each autumn the Pearly Kings and Queens came to our school. One would sit at the piano and gently crack his knuckles. Cross-legged on the parquet floor we held hands, sometimes even were allowed to stand up and awkwardly dance. We threw our knees up to '*Mother Brown*', became misty eyed at '*Maybe It's Because I'm a Londoner*', did the 'Lambeth Walk'. My parents were not born in London, my mother isn't British. My fellow pupils spoke English as their second, third, fourth languages. They came here not for the clean air and rolling hills, long gone by the mid 1980s, but because there were council homes for them. That was why I was there too. There was a home for my family in Edgware when there wasn't one anywhere else in the city. Behind each of our families was a story that ran back through a movie's worth of drama. And each one ended here in a new house in a new town.

On the edges of the town where countryside and city wash into each other is a nature reserve, the Welsh Harp. As a child, I would pick brambles there and fill carrier bags with their plump motorway-dust-flecked bodies. Beyond the edges of the reservoir stood Stonegrove Estate, its beige tower blocks swept upwards out of the rushes. They're gone now. Nine hundred and ninety-nine homes moved onwards in the name of regeneration. My family never lived on that estate. It was ugly and dirty and dangerous. Still I cried when I saw the last tower block being knocked down. The estate, like the town, was ours. We lived here. Those were homes given to us as gifts. They showed that someone, somewhere, cared about us, whoever we were. Now, when I look out from the Welsh Harp, there is nothing. The town is turning its back on us. Along the parade shops are boarded up and office windows cloud with dust. The town's low flat roofs still move across the crests of hills but now are overshadowed by trees. I see us cycling backwards, through time, towards the fields and the streams and the trackway. Towards the thick wet dark soil that I plunge my hands into, fingers wriggling alongside worms. We lived here. In this nothing and nowhere place, each of us stopped for a moment. Now we no longer need the town, it no longer needs us. If Edgware still exists in a decade's time it will be in the stories we tell of climbing over tyres stacked high by railway sidings, or the smell of cooking caught on a summer's breeze. Edgware isn't a shithole, never was, never will be. Edgware isn't anything. Edgware simply is.

IN BIRTH

Tori Truslow

Today I gave my child a mouth.

A mother's first gift. I pushed a thumb into the skin – strange to feel that soft impression of mine suddenly quicken and suck. The midwife's hands were on my arms. 'Up to your breast,' she said, 'yes, that's it.'

The unshaped flesh moved against me, finding and latching to the teat. My hands full with warmth and instinct. They seemed to know what to do, where to hold and how to press, sharp beating in my breast marking unknown time until after hours or maybe minutes this person in my arms has the beginning of a shape.

'So sure, so natural! It's not always the way with new mothers,' beams the midwife. 'And such a sweet round mouth!'

A mother's first gift, we call it. Why the mouth, why not the shaping that comes before birth, or after? Why not *birth*? Because birthing is a duty, a suffering, or – if our great poet is correct – a theft? He wrote: *In the womb I grew arms, legs, fingers, even lips! / In birth I was robbed of my face.*

He was one of those who believe we begin fully formed, our features erased by the pressures of birth. Even in that, a mother can only go wrong.

A mouth is hard to get wrong.

39

The priest has come, and sits by my bed with one long palm held to my child's head, the other on my hand. *Don't touch*, I hold myself back from saying.

'Today you have received the holy task of giving shape to life,' he says, and raises his hand from my child, towards the stone figures on the shelf above the doorway. 'Pray the gods show you a child of true form."

I open my mouth but before I can raise words on it he lays his mix of glistening salts and herbs on my tongue and I drop back to the pillow like a stone.

* * *

(There is a rainless blue storm flashing over the hills, and underneath I wander in streets that fold and unfold to reveal the shapes of everything forgotten, half-seen. I reach a corner where the flesh of some bloody, sabre-toothed thing crackles in a wide oven, turns its sockets on me and says *come inside, wrap me with your thighs, and I will whisper you a true child's form*. I see the muscle melting from its bones and ache to join but the heat won't let me get near so I pull out my guts as a love-token and run.)

* * *

When I wake, the midwife tells me my child is becoming a girl.

'Did you dream a face for her? Do you want me to show you how to shape it just right?'

I open my mouth but once again I can't say anything.

I never wanted this. I don't know who this is that I'm holding, how can I know what shape is right?

I shake my head.

The midwife throws open the doors, and cries, 'A daughter!'

* * *

Friends are all around me now, telling me what they've seen around the town, showing pictures of what's fashionable this year. One gives me a gift of pearls, for a child born under a full moon.

A full moon daughter is beautiful.

A full moon daughter sings and is fertile.

Press pearls into her brow so the world will know.

She stirs in my arms, reaches for me with the buds of limbs. She cries, without tears, without eyes.

* * *

The story we're told is this:

There was a woman who wandered over the black stone hills, far from her home, where she could never find a husband. She walked until dry hunger and wind-driven thirst cracked her like splintering slate. And as the sun was setting she saw a standing shape and thought it to be shelter, though it was only an empty well.

She approached it and dropped to her knees, asking for sanctuary.

Oh, but deep within the well there was a man and oh, but he was not a man. A slumbering spirit, lying under the last of the mud, which his dreams pulled around him to make muscle and he moved, slick and sliding, boneless and dripping, roused by her voice, climbing from the well to look upon her.

41

His fingers cold and wet, her skin hot and cracked. He whispered to her in the drawing dark and took her in his chilling arms under the cold moon. She birthed clay children at dawn and shaped them into human forms but the sun and wind baked them hard before she could make them beautiful. Their father dried in the day to lie cracked under their feet, and their mother walked on, for they were new things and would not love her.

And the children, they got up and built a city.

There are many variations on this tale, but this is the one the priests call true

***

(I have walked and walked these streets and never seen a form that fits you, but still I come back every time my eyes fall closed. Now I make my way among trailing night flowers, under houses that have been gnawed by great-jawed things. My body is empty, you should be here with me but you're hidden somewhere. I can hear your heart beating, where is it? Is it that white stone in the sky?

I walk between the beast-eaten walls, where windows watch like children.

Perhaps around the next corner, I'll find you.)

***

My mother is at my bedside, a branching arm spread across my body.

She is exquisite, so she made me plain. She says her dreams showed her my shape as it should be, but I think she gave me practical form – just two thick arms, two long legs, shoulders broad as well as hips, a shape people call manlike – in long-harboured protest against all her fragile fronds. She always swears she shaped me herself. What time and pain it must have taken, with those dainty leaflike fingers.

Now she urges balance, tells me to make my child strong, but lovely.

I can't bear to hear her waver on the edge of apology, for making me unbeautiful, for making me at all. Hear her unspoken conviction that it's her fault I was alone for so long, and her fault that the husband I found is in her eyes rough and strange.

It's not you, it was never you. I don't say it because it's only half true. I've resented her in my time, but I'm glad of it too.

I never wanted this.

The man I married cuts stone in the hills. His mother pressed flat round stones into the surface of his skin, to make him a tough worker and a hard target, protected from animals' teeth and the weapons of men. Too heavy for many girls to bear, and even with me he has to be cautious.

As he grew, he carved flowers and foliage into his stones; as the gaps of skin between the stones grew too, he joined them with tattooed vines. He hates his form, and loves it. I used to sit up with him all night, both of us finding comfort in comparing these feelings.

He has been out in the hills for days now, unaware his child has been born. And I don't know, if he was here, what we would say to each other. What all our conversations would mean, now.

My mother tries to hold the child. Was it this hard for her to hold me? All her limbs like fine fronds.

43

My mind is running like a dancer with her ribbons unravelling, and the cloth is torn and the threads are many. The threads catch on the girls inlaid with precious jewels and fine tiles, who sit on cushions and hardly move. On the poor girls patterned with broken glass instead. Sometimes it juts out of them, and any man who touched them would shred his palms. Until they marry, and the shards are cut out.

There are races to make the most elaborate children before the skin firms.

'Here's the truth,' says my mother. 'Your dreams will only show you half of it. You still have to choose what you take from them.' She withdraws her arms. 'Look at me. Look at you. And look at her. I know it's frightening, but you must give her a form.'

***

(I follow the trail of scent from someone cooking, between the twisting angles of the houses. Wafts of it come on the warm moving air, too thick and slow to call a breeze. The dusty dry night strikes a hunger in my empty insides but I'm getting no closer to the source. There are spices and simmering meat. Sweat wells on my brow, on my lip, I lick but it's not salty enough to sate me.

Who is it that's cooking? Only now I see all the houses are dark, the streets untrodden. The city's starting to cool, a film of unease forming over it like grease. The warm, sweet smell is rolling down from the hills, where the beasts stir at a bulging pot of tender spiced flesh, not to eat but to melt down and re-form into better prey.

I run, to beg – for what? A bowl, or to be allowed to join

the pot, to let my meat unravel and be made anew by the beasts' ragged paws?)

* * *

She won't stop wailing. I've fed her but she wants more, wants fingers to grasp at me with. But what kind of fingers? The midwife gave me a harsh look this morning: *you are letting her flesh stiffen unshaped.* She looks over at me again and shakes her head. What a disappointment I must be to her, who had called me a natural.

It has to be soon. Tomorrow, or the day after, so I can take her out in the sun and let her flesh start to firm. To let her start growing into herself.

We all pretend it's glorious, it's wonderful. We give thanks for it, call it a gift. To take all we've learned and dreamed and put it into someone new.

We say it's joyous. Even though we've all heard the stories, mothers who've torn their children into pieces, and trampled the pieces and cast them into the fire, because you swallow the fear of making them wrong until it's stuffed all the way down your throat making it impossible to breathe.

Only stories, we always say. *Who could truly do that? Not you, no; not I.*

* * *

(I've found no form for you, my child, though I've searched every corner of this dreaming city. Every corner but one – and surely it would be blasphemous to take an image from this place. To even presume to step inside.

45

But the gods are always changing their faces, aren't they, and who's to stop me taking one, soon to be discarded, to be forgotten by the time the rains have ended?

No one, not here, inside my own heart. So in I step.

I come to a courtyard where three figures sit, familiar and foreign all at once. Their skin splits open along invisible seams to show the pulsing clay underneath, which then hardens to hide and then to stone again, and they are so ancient and full of forms that they split and glisten and dry continually.

I walk to the last god, the youngest, who is splitting at the belly. Grasp the soft flesh underneath, shape it with these thick fingers into a face as best I can as the earthy blood congeals like leathery red gloves on my hands.

But it is not your face. Its skin splits open and I pull out handfuls of godflesh and fan them into fronds and fins and it all keeps bursting open and re-forming under these heavy blood-gloved hands.

You must be in here somewhere.)

***

I wake to find that my hands have been working.

She is like me, and yet not. And still unfinished, but with ears and nose and eyelids, and dreaming eyes beneath. It's different to the face in my own dreams, but there's something of the temple in it. Something of the ever-changing gods.

I wish I could see your dreams, I think, and then almost laugh for the first time since the birth. *As if I'd understand them.*

We are alone, at last, still and quiet against each other. So I start to speak, softly; tell her everything in my heart. All the answerless questions I've ever put to anyone, or no-one. All the trepidation for questions I might get asked one day. And the hope – that they will get asked, and that I'll know how to hear them.

She wakes softly, opens her eyes and stares. The mouth I pressed into being opens too, makes a sound I can't name or interpret.

I try to speak back, clumsy-tongued, in this between-language that we must build between us. A mother's first gift, they call it, but it's not.

It's our first collaboration.

BRAID MY HAIR

Zahrah Nesbitt-Ahmed

Maryam couldn't have been older than eighteen when we first met. Then again, I was only thirteen when she came into my life – my sense of people's age was non-existent. Maryam lived in our estate in Ikeja a few doors down. I don't know how my mother found out she braided – maybe word of mouth from someone in the neighbourhood. All I know is after the debacle of my first outside braiding experience I was hesitant to have anyone but my mother – my trusted hairstylist from birth – touch my hair.

* * *

'Aunty, Aunty! Do your hair?' was shouted by different women and men as I entered the world of Ikeja under bridge with my mother. I held on to her hand as tightly as I could for fear of being separated and getting lost in the buzz of activities as we walked under the poorly lit flyovers. 'Aunty, Aunty! Come and buy hair.' 'Colour 1B.' 'Colour 2.' We continued to weave through the sea of people looking for clientele. All around me was the hustle and bustle of the city. 'Gala, Gala.' Others briskly walking by or haggling for one thing or the other in the makeshift shops on either side of the road. There were newspaper and magazine vendors, secondhand-book sellers and those who sold food and clothes. Danfos picking up and dropping commuters on the service lane right under the bridge; young men as conductors calling for passengers by shouting the destinations at the top of their lungs: 'Opebi-Allen, Agege, Apapa-Wharf, Iyana-Ipaja, Ketu.'

The hair salons, also situated outside, were dark and bare boned. Plastic chairs for the braiders, with wooden benches for the customers to sit on. Prices were no more than one hundred naira and the braiders had what they needed to get the job done. Dark-brown, three-pronged wooden combs for parting the hair into sections. Thick petroleum-based hair grease laced with a heavy natural scent to mask the range of chemicals in it – blue-green in colour, there would always be a blob of this grease on their hands to scoop and run along the scalp on each section of parted hair. Scissors to cut the hair extensions into the necessary length at the start of the process and to snip away stray hairs from the extensions at the end of the process. Shards of broken glass used as mirrors for the customers to marvel at their new hairstyle once the job was done. Candles – if needed – lit at the end of the braiding process to burn the tips of the hair, so the braid would not unravel.

It was the late 1990s. I had experimented with pigtails, canerows, colourful hair clips, bubbles and scrunchies – all done during the weekends by my British-Caribbean mother, with me sitting between her legs on our living room floor, the both of us singing to a mix of Beres Hammond, Maxi Priest, Luther Vandross, SWV, Jodeci. I was ready for a bigger-girl hairstyle – one more mature, one with extensions.

I had grown up seeing women, including many an aunt and older cousin, with their hair braided into amazing styles.

Some with extensions, others without. Wealthier women would pay thousands of naira to get their hair braided in high-end salons all over the city. Women from lower- and middle-income classes could be found in places like Ikeja under bridge getting the latest styles at a more affordable price. I was now joining this world.

By this time, over in Western countries, braided bobs had been made popular by Brandy Norwood – whom my adolescent self adored. There was also Dionne, Stacey Dash's character in *Clueless*, as well as the Jamaican reggae and dancehall artist Patra, but their braids were longer. As I got older, I would learn that the era also saw Jada Pinkett Smith rocking a braided bob in the movie *Set It Off*, Regina King with large box braids in *Boyz n the Hood*, and, of course, Janet Jackson's famous *Poetic Justice* braids. Yet, in my world in Ikeja, hair braiding was simply a part of our everyday existence – one that had been practised in various African societies for centuries. Some say it goes as far back as 500 BC, going from Egypt around the Nile Valley before moving to other parts of the African continent, including among the Fulani, Bantu, Hausa and Yoruba people. In many communities, braid patterns were reflective of where someone was from, their marital status, social status and even age.

Within Nigeria, with its hundreds of ethnic groups and multiple languages, the uniqueness and rich cultural traditions around hairstyles are perfectly captured in the work of Nigerian photographer Johnson Donatus Aihumekeokhai Ojeikere, known as J.D. 'Okhai Ojeikere. Ojeikere's collection of a thousand photographs spanning forty years show that hairstyles in the Nigerian context range from being purely decorative to symbols with precise meanings.[1] There are also styles worn on a regular basis and ones made particularly for special occasions, such as weddings or birthdays. For Ojeikere, 'the hairstyles are never exactly the same; each one has its own beauty'.[2] For me, I was simply excited to be trying something new.

The braided bob was the style I was going for. I might have been old enough for hair extensions, but not for long braids – that wouldn't be for another few years. I sat down on the uncomfortable wooden benches, unaware that would be my existence for the next four hours. There were three women braiding my hair, ensuring my head was simultaneously pulled in different directions. They each parted off a small section of my hair, applied the blue-green grease to my scalp, took the extensions and wrapped them around my hair, then braided it in three sections from my roots down to the ends of my hair. Once done, then came the snip, snip, snip of the scissors to get rid of the stray hairs. Then to secure the braids at the ends, the tips were burned with a candle. The shards of broken glass came out. 'Fine girl.' It was done. I was no longer being pulled in multiple directions. Having never had extensions I worried, during the snipping of the stray hairs, about whether some of my real hair got snipped, and in the burning of the tips whether some of my hair burned. My head was sore with my scalp feeling the most tender it had ever felt. I had a throbbing headache. I felt like crying. No-one had told me this rite of passage came with so much pain. Less than four weeks later, the braided bob was gone. So too a lot of my own hair. It was the first and last time I experienced Ikeja under bridge.

1 J. D. 'Okhai Ojeikere: Hairstyles and Headresses, New Art Exchange http://www.nae.org.uk/exhibition/jd-okhai-ojeikere-hairstyles-and/66
2 ibid

***

It was 2000. It must have been a Sunday afternoon. As always there was no electricity when Maryam arrived at our home. I would be braiding my hair outside, at the front of the house where it would be cooler. Under an archway in a covered area, in case it rained, with trees on either side of us. I was nervous and, if I am honest, suspicious. Was Maryam going to treat my hair, my scalp, my edges in the same way the women at Ikeja under bridge did?

Until that afternoon, my mother had resumed her role as my trusted hairstylist. My hair had also been restored to its pre-Ikeja under bridge state. I don't remember what made me want to let someone else into my life again to braid my hair. Maybe it was wanting to be more independent, or to look more mature, older. I am not sure. This time, I would be at home. It would be safer, more pleasurable. This time, I was aware of the experience, prepared for what was to come.

I grabbed two chairs from the dining room, dragging them to the front door – scraping the tiles on the floor in the corridor as I did. Maryam smiled at me – a smile that I would come to associate with her during the times she braided my hair. I asked her if she wanted anything – water, a soft drink, juice, biscuits. She asked me to sit down.

On our first day, nothing much was said between the two of us. Maryam stood while I sat on one of the dining table chairs. Over time, as we got to know each other and as such became more comfortable, she would sit on the dining table chair while I sat on a smaller pouch. An hour and a half later, she was done. My hair in a Fulani-inspired all back style. It was perfect for school – it could be put in a low bun, out

53

of the way. At the weekend, I would wear it down with the braids free and hanging loose. Being older meant my extensions could be slightly longer than they had been previously. I hadn't looked at myself in the mirror yet, but I knew my head didn't hurt. Maryam didn't pull at my scalp too tightly or in multiple directions, which had previously been the norm. There was no headache. Could it be?

I ran in to ask my mum for the money. Her face said it all: the style was gorgeous. I briefly stopped to glance at myself in the mirror. I smiled – it was great, but I didn't love it. I have never been a fan of freshly done braids, with my hair, scalp and sometimes even my forehead looking shiny from the hair grease. Yet, I knew that in a week, when it was a little older and worn in, I would be in love with it. I handed Maryam the money and thanked her. She smiled.

Maryam smelt like a mix of coconut and oud. Like her smile, it too became something I associated with her, and a scent that to this day makes me think solely of her whenever I get a rare whiff of it. An extremely attractive Shuwa-Arab woman with a petite frame, fine features and gorgeous natural hair always neatly canerowed, her fingertips were red from laali. Like the women at Ikeja under bridge, Maryam also had a three-pronged wooden comb for parting the hair into sections. Unlike the women under the bridge, Maryam's hands were a wonder: she braided my hair so softly it often felt like she wasn't even touching it.

The braiders at Ikeja under bridge were the first to make me aware of the important relationship between my hair and my edges, but it was Maryam who showed me the beauty of a trusting relationship with a great braider. With each visit to my home, each parting of strands of my hair, each passing of separated pieces of hair extensions, each row braided softly, my feelings of entrusting Maryam with my hair became stronger. I loved the craft involved in the styles she created for my head. I loved getting my hair braided by her.

Maryam would arrive at my house on Sunday afternoons, at a time usually specified by her. I was an awkward teenager: a deep thinker and always lost in my thoughts, but being around Maryam made me open up, made me more trusting towards strangers. It wasn't necessarily because we had deep and meaningful conversations. Sometimes we would talk about movies and music, fashion and hairstyles. Sometimes, I simply wanted to sit down, hand over the extensions and read a book, while she worked for a couple of hours braiding my hair.

My trust was rooted in the fact that I knew she wouldn't hurt my scalp or damage my hair. I knew she would make me feel beautiful. The ability to sit back, and trust that the braider understands you and your scalp, is a special luxury. This is not a universal experience for Black women, where many an edge has been snatched from the tension of the braids. On the contrary, Maryam set the standards in which I let other women style my hair even to this day. Yet, one day she was gone with little warning. I knew that no-one else would come close, so I stopped getting braided extensions.

* * *

A few years into the noughties, my mother said I could come with her to the hairdressers. I was about to enter the world of styling units and styling chairs, hair being washed, conditioned and rinsed in basins at washpoints, hooded hair dryers,

women and older teenage girls gossiping. It was there Aunty
Fatimah came into my life. A dark-skinned Yoruba woman in
her thirties with the most infectious laugh, a lot of women at
the salon wanted her to braid their hair, and they always left
with a smile. My mother enquired and an appointment was
made. Again, I was cautious and hesitant.

Aunty Fatimah suggested Ghana weaving at the front, with
single braids at the back. I had never heard of the style and
was nervous about trying something new that might not suit
me. Little did I know it would become my go-to braided look
for the next ten years. As I sat on the styling chair, with a red
towel held with a clip draped over my shoulder, Aunty Fatimah
handed me the hair extensions that had been cut in three.

My hair was sectioned into two – the front for the Ghana
weaving, and around three-quarters of the back for the single
braids. She asked me for small parts of hair extensions and
divided them into three, folding one layer of hair over the
other part, to start the braid, tapping me on my shoulder if I
was too slow in handing her another small part of extension
for the next two to three rows. This continued until the first
braid was done, to create a beautiful layer of braids. I had
never seen anything like that. I marvelled at the intricacies
and beauty of the braid. I continued handing Aunty Fatimah
small parts of hair extension. Three hours later, she was done.
Again, I glanced at myself in the mirror, and smiled. Aunty
Fatimah also had soft hands, braiding my hair like it was a
delicate piece of china that couldn't be broken.

Having experienced this feeling of softness with two different hair braiders, I was now certain that beauty was not pain
when it came to braiding with extensions – especially after my
unpleasant Ikeja under bridge time. I also did not need to be

silent and endure that pain. This realisation was significant, as being a so-called tender-headed child, my mother was already extra careful when doing my hair to minimise as much as possible the wincing that often came with washing, drying and styling. I was not going to take this privilege of comfort afforded to me by Aunty Fatimah (and previously Maryam) for granted.

Yet Aunty Fatimah wasn't in my life for long. She was pregnant, and after giving birth, set up her own small salon in an area too far for my family to access. Still, she taught me what it means to take a leap of faith and trust something outside your control. In getting me to try a style I had never heard of, she took me out of my comfort zone. Less than a year after Aunty Fatimah came into my life, she was gone. I was starting to wonder, was I destined to find great braiders who would love me and leave me?

Probably sensing my sadness at losing her, Aunty Fatimah introduced my mother to her apprentice – a young woman called Jumai. I had noticed Jumai at the hairdressers. Washing hair, sweeping up and folding away towels, and braiding only the ends of hair. Jumai was in her early twenties, Yoruba, and small in stature. She was also easier to speak to, becoming my gisting buddy during our braiding sessions at the hairdressers. Over time, as we got to know each other, I learned that Jumai used to be a domestic worker before her employer got her an apprenticeship at the salon. She was saving up to go to Yaba Polytechnic College, and also did home services for hair to earn extra money.

By the mid-noughties, I was in the UK. Unlike Maryam and Aunty Fatimah, Jumai would be the braider who I ended up knowing the longest – eight years, as I only ever called her when I was back in Lagos. Having loved and lost two braiders already, I wasn't about to lose another one.

***

The UK was new territory for me when it came to braids. The first shock was the prices. In Ikeja, I would pay the equivalent of £15 to £20, which by Lagos standards was on the higher end. In London, the cheapest place I found was £50 for the standard size. 'If you want it longer and bigger, it's more.' My first winter, a salon with African women braiders in Seven Sisters charged me £60 for Ghana weaving. It was a difficult price to pay, especially as it reminded me more of the Ikeja under bridge experience than the salon with Aunty Fatimah. That should have been the first warning, but I wanted to get my hair braided. Their hands weren't soft – the second warning. Again, I persisted. A headache ensued post-braiding. Six weeks later, taking the braids out, I was transported to my younger self. My hair fell out in chunks while removing the braids. By the time I was done, my ends were weak and my edges were non-existent.

My first decade in the country was a period of not being satisfied with the braiders I found. I continued to wander aimlessly in search of the right one – another salon in Seven Sisters was recommended, as well as one in Norwood Junction. It was really a time of failure and heartbreak. The only person who could live up to my expectations was Jumai, but that could only happen when I returned home to Lagos. Over time those trips back home became increasingly sporadic. Wanting to free myself from searching for the right stylist in the UK, 2013 saw me making the decision to learn how to do my hair myself – to canerow it, to twist with extensions. I did my first set of individuals by myself at twenty-six – kinky twists. It took me an entire weekend. Stopping and starting, doing and re-doing was a tenuous process, but the result was that I was able to do my hair myself. Again, I glanced at myself in the mirror, and smiled – it was great, but I didn't love it. I knew I would in a week's time. More than that, I felt a sense of relief: I would not have to endure the thankless task of searching for the right braider again.

***

However, something changed. In 2016 – almost two decades since the first time I had my hair braided with extensions – I decided to give braiders in London one last chance. What changed? My mother had found a place in Croydon owned by a Ghanaian man with Ghanaian stylists. Maybe that was the missing link all these years. With the exception of Ikeja under bridge, the three braiders that have treated my hair with love and tenderness have all come into my life through my mother.

The décor at the salon is yellow and black, with no artwork except for two vintage hairstyle posters in the waiting area. It operates on a first-come-first-served basis. Every time I go there, there are always a few women impatiently waiting for the store to open, hoping to be first in line to have their hair done.

I've been going there two to three times a year, fluctuating between two hairstyles – kinky twists or bum-length chunky box braids, all single plaits. With the box braids, the braider takes the packet of extensions from me – Expressions, Colour 1B – cutting it into two sections, feathering the tips of each section of the extensions in preparation for braiding. Once done, each section is divided into smaller, manageable sections which are loosely tied and handed over to me. My hair is sectioned, chunky strands of the extensions are handed to the braider, while they gossip and share stories with each other in their own language. Depending on the style, the process takes four to six hours. At the end, the stray bits are snipped away, and the ends of the braids dipped in boiling water to seal them.

Chatting with these Ghanaian women – who have moved to London for a better life for themselves, and sometimes their children – gives me a different insight into hair braiding, one that was grossly missing in my younger years. The skill of braiding hair provides a source of income and a hope that it will be a bridge to a better life for many of these women, but it also comes with its challenges.

Many women rent chairs in the salon and work long hours – 10am to 7pm, six days a week, sometimes on Sundays (by appointment only) and on holidays, with short breaks in between for lunch or snacks. It's also a demanding job – physically and mentally. Have you ever watched a braider in action – how fast their hands move as they braid? They work at the same pace and consistency for many hours a day with many customers, leading to pain in many parts of their body – wrists, back, shoulders. My younger self did not fully comprehend these aspects of hair braiding – worrying more about minimising the pain I was feeling and not whether the braider experienced pain, and what I could do (if anything) to minimise it for them, such as using extensions that are less harsh on their fingers and wrists.

Despite the occasional feeling of a braider pulling too tight on my scalp (which I now remind them not to do), after all these years of searching, I might have found a home for my braids. I love the fact that I only have to deal with my hair being braided once every two or three months. There's a level of convenience – being able to wake up and not spend too long in the morning deciding what I will do with my hair. There's also the extra time daily I get to focus on other aspects of my life. Even though the braids still need to be taken down, which can often be a long and arduous process, I will continue sitting for hours in homes or at salons having my hair – hopefully – gently braided by Black women because this is an integral part of me.

COMMUNITY — Marian Sloane

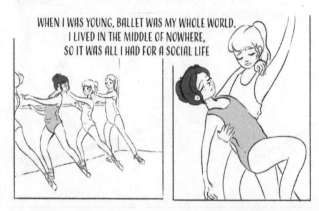

GROWING UP IN A SMALL COMMUNITY, I DIDN'T HAVE ANY EXPOSURE TO QUEER CULTURE. THE ONLY TIME I HEARD THE WORD GAY WAS AS A PLAYGROUND INSULT.

SO I PUSHED AWAY EVERYONE I CARED ABOUT ...

AND ALL THE THINGS I LOVED.

IT WASN'T TILL I WAS AROUND FIFTEEN THAT I ACTUALLY FOUND LESBIANS IN A YOUNG ADULT NOVEL. IT SOUNDS DRAMATIC, BUT IT'S FAIR TO SAY IT PROBABLY SAVED MY LIFE.

I DIDN'T HAVE ACCESS TO A 'REAL LIFE' COMMUNITY AROUND ME.

BUT THE CHARACTERS IN THE STORIES GAVE ME HOPE.

AND HELPED ME FIND FRIENDS AROUND THE WORLD.

WITHOUT YA FICTION, I MIGHT NEVER HAVE FOUND OTHERS LIKE ME AND I CERTAINLY WOULDN'T HAVE LEARNT TO ACCEPT MYSELF.

THERE IS STILL A WAY TO GO IN TERMS OF REPRESENTATION, BUT EVERY YEAR BRINGS US MORE STORIES.

AND I'LL NEVER STOP GETTING EXCITED FOR ALL THE YOUNG QUEER TEENS WHO ARE ABLE TO READ ABOUT THEMSELVES FOR THE FIRST TIMES

BECAUSE WHILST IT'S JUST STRINGS OF WORDS ON PAGES, IT SHOWS US WHEVEVER WE ARE WE'RE NOT ALONE.

OLIVE BRANCH

Maz Hedgehog

I am facing you,
Your skin gleaming like granite or maple,
Sharp eyed, sharp boned --
I had cut myself on the curve of
Your lip more times than I
Care to remember.
Back when sweet nothings turned to
Sickly, overripe fruit I thought
You must be made of cold iron, of
Dreamless sleep and growing old but
I never did bother to learn
Your name as well as you did mine.

I breathe in the pine trees we chose
For this new thing. I look at you,
You look back and I think we can both taste
The kisses that sealed our meetings.
I don't know how to greet you anymore.
I try hello, offer you
Olive leaves and yellow roses.
You take them into your lap and reply
'Good morrow', stiff and hoarse.

Maz Hedgehog

Your voice doesn't sound like
A lost soul at midnight anymore.
You clear your throat, say it again.
I say it to you, as unguarded as I can.
Your face lights up and the sight
Doesn't fill my skin to bursting with
Memories of satyrs at the equinox or
Selkies on a winter's eve.

We touch fingers and share mushrooms,
Mirror grins for half a moment.
We're not strangers;
We've lured too many young lovers
Given too much goblin fruit and
Ensnared too many children to be strangers
But we don't share a tongue anymore.
We make a bargain, trace new knots into the bark
Of the trees in the grove around us.
This will not be the end, just a change.
It will not be lesser,
It will not trap us
It will not hinder or diminish us.
We will not swallow ourselves,
Not for new grass,
Not for nightmares,
Not for all the
Fresh milk and new pennies
In the world.

DINNER, AT THE TABLE

Lexi Earl

You regularly tell me how poor you are, how little money you have after you've paid rent and bills. I offer to send you some. You always refuse. Absolutely. Resolutely. You have been stubborn since you were tiny. You are determined to make it on your own. Without help. I sigh at the circular nature of our conversation, and then simply turn up with sourdough bread. Fig jam. Homemade salted caramel spread. Dark chocolate brownies with cacao nibs. I include edible gifts for your birthday and Christmas – this year it was hot chocolate and marshmallows. You accept the gifts with enthusiasm. They are not exactly practical, nutritionally, but they provide fuel and I worry less about you going hungry at night. Plus, the lack of nutritional value means it appears these are to supplement your normal meals, rather than provide them, so you accept.

Occasionally I turn up with bags full of groceries. I stock your fridge. You do not object. Somehow the fact that this isn't money seems to make it different. You don't have a freezer. If you did, I would batch cook meals, portion them into tupperwares, and drive down to the big smoke to hide them amongst the non-existent frozen peas.

Whenever we are together we eat and drink. We celebrate

our lives through meals shared at a table. They say family meals are the birthplace of civilisation. Or Michael Pollan does anyway. There are supposed to be benefits to eating at the table: we eat 'properly', eat the right things, learn to share. To behave in a particular manner. I am sure there are those benefits. There must be plenty of people with whom this resonates, who think the solution to all our health/food/weight/societal problems starts at the table, at the beginning of things.

I have many memories of tables, and food, and sharing. Perhaps you do too? Whenever I think of family dinners, I think of childhood summers at Jevington, Old Sam's farm in the Free State. Those were glorious, carefree days of childhood when we were left mostly to look after each other, to roam without boundaries, and to work our own ways out of scrapes and scratches. The dining room table in Trude and Bruce's house was that extra-long, incredibly heavy, dark teak table with matching chairs. I think there were twelve chairs, something that I always found incredible. When would you ever need to feed so many people all at once? Our small table for six seemed miniscule in comparison. The table was assembled in the room, and Mom used to joke how they would have to either leave it in the house (because what other house could possibly have a room large enough for that table?) or they would have to dismantle it and take it piece by piece, if they ever moved to a new home. Of course it was a joke because they would obviously never live anywhere else.

Meals at that table were either extremely relaxed affairs with everyone coming to eat together, or frenzied passings of toast while making for the door in order to get to school on time. But I was never in a rush at that table. It was a table for holidays, not for rushing to school and workplaces. I liked it there. I liked watching people coming and going. I liked being able to linger over porridge. You always sat halfway out of your seat, already on your way elsewhere. I was always trying to slow you down, make you wait, let me finish before we went gallivanting off on horseback. Everyone came back to eat together at lunchtime too. I loved that.

Those meals were a sharp contrast to what happened at home, during term time. At home, our parents were at work all day, and so the focus was the evening meal. Lunch we ate either at school, or with Janet, our nanny. Dad insisted we eat around the table almost every night of the week. Fridays were an exception when we could get takeaways, and watch a movie.

You are too young to remember very clearly that time before our parents were divorced. Or maybe you have blocked it out? We never ate out a lot. For most of our childhoods, our parents couldn't really afford that I don't think. Once, a cousin came to stay, and he complained that we were always eating 'yesterday's food'. Mom was big on leftovers.

When they told us they were separating, it took ages for Dad to move out. He had to wait on a property he was buying. They slept in separate bedrooms. That day they told us he said, 'We will eat dinner at the table together. Like a proper family.' Or something to that effect anyway. Do you remember? I do. Because I thought, 'What proper family?' Those dinners were excruciating.

The divorce broke all the plates we ate on (if not actually, at least figuratively).

After, we did not sit at the table any more. I was not at home for long, I left for university before the divorce was finalised. But something about the table was broken. You told me that you and Mom used to eat in the kitchen, or in front of the television, wolfing down ready-meals or snack foods between ballet classes, rowing sessions and horse riding. Janet had left us by then so there was no-one at home to cook. When I moved back again I cooked. But we still did not really eat at the table, even though we were in a different house. We threw dinner parties a lot. I cooked three-course meals for many friends. We mostly ate at the table outside. But when it was just the two or three of us, we ate on the couch.

Mom gave that table to a cousin eventually. She has a new one now. We eat there.

You and I eat at the table when we are together now. And we cook together. Despite family rumours that you do not know how to cook, you are perfectly capable if so inclined. You even make a mean cheesecake.

CAMBRIC

Mikael Johani

translated by Anya Rompas

[Editors Note: This poem was translated by Anya Rompas, Mikael Johani's wife, from the original Indonesian.]

—terdampar lagi di kamar ini
wallpaper motif trellis
mengelupas di sana sini
dua lampu sorot
tepat di atas kepala
lubang angin berbentuk hati
layang layang tanpa ekor
di langit sana

—langit di sini selalu biru
Pantone 292

—bukan misteri juga
sebenarnya seandainya
aku bisa mencegah menciumnya
di pojok bar gelap

Mikael Johani

dan seminggu kemudian
bilang ya saja
waktu dia menuntut
kita tidak bisa begini terus
kan gila

—tapi memang
sekali layang layang putus tali
tak ada yang mau benar benar tahu
siapa kini menaikkannya kembali

—mungkin juga tinggal rangka
gering di pucuk angsana

—kejar mengejar ada mangsanya
sekarang telah tiba
musim instan
benang telah digelas
layang layang berekor
bertelinga

—kalau hidup bisa seperti berburu
bukit hijau padang savanna
Afrika Sumbawa

—berhenti
(begitu saja)
peluru menembus kepala
atau hati?

—belajarlah anatomi!

74

—semua hanya khayal semata
dan kata orang
32 waktunya beranjak dewasa

—aku pun sadar itu

—ada saatnya
turunkan ayunan
menggantung dasi
sebagai gantinya

—mana mungkin ada
hidup tanpa autopsi
hanya penyembelihan
diikuti makan pesta pora
di depan api unggun
tangan tangan merah hitam
diusapkan ke celana

—tidak!
hidup penuh post-mortem
segalanya
perhitungan gono gini
siapa yang membayar liburan ke Bali
siapa yang waktu itu ragu ragu pergi
cinta siapa yang lebih sejati?

—baik kau biasakan
aku biasakan
naik banding
ke Mahkamah Percintaan

Mikael Johani

dengan kau sebagai
Hakim Ketua
Hakim I
Hakim II
Jaksa
Pembela

—aku sekedar pesakitan
di kursi berpunggung rotan

—di laporan koran esok hari
hanya foto punggungku yang diedarkan

—penjahat memang harus dihindari

—takut menular!

—Dewan Hakim Yang Mulia
ampunilah aku
karena aku tak tahu pun
apa yang telah kulakukan
aku tahu ini bukan alasan
apalagi alibi yang tak bisa dibantahkan
aku hanya menuntut
belas kasihan-Mu
karena aku manusia
tak tahu malu

—seandainya hidup
sesentimentil bayanganku!

—sekarang, ingat ingat ini,
catat kalau bisa
di blocnoot murahan pun tak apa
asal "kwaliteit baik":
kau sedang duduk duduk di Popi's
kedai kecil di Gondangdia Lama
menonton kereta Bogor
melintasi bulan
lengan lengan
menggantung keluar
dari pintunya
dan hidup rasanya
seperti inilah seharusnya
selamanya

—masukkan Selected Poems
Williams-mu ke dalam tas
tak usah kunci tutupnya
ini kan hanya simbolik saja
toh kau sudah hapal
di luar kepala
The Widow's Lament in Springtime
atau apapun dari
Journey to Love
(bukankah manis
epigrafnya:
"For My Wife"
—"the whole process is a lie"!—
this whole poem is a lie

(—unless, paling tidak di kota ini

Mikael Johani

kau selalu kembali ke rumah
walau kau juga yang merusaknya)

* * *

—stranded again in this room
its fleur de lys wallpaper
peeling here and there
two spotlights
right above my head
a heart-shaped vent
a kite missing its tail
floating in the distant sky

—here the sky is always blue
Pantone 292

—not a mystery really
what if
i had held back from kissing her
in that dark corner of a bar
and then a week later
just said yeah let's
when she demanded
this has got to stop
we're gonna drive ourselves crazy
(we're gonna drive ourselves crazy)

—but yeah
once a kite loses its tail
everybody loses interest

who will fly it again?

—a withered kite, stripped to its frame
stuck on top of an angsana tree

—there's a season to hunt
and be hunted
now is the season for
instant everything
we've dipped the thread
in broken glass
the kite has a new tail
a new set of ears

—life is like a hunting party
a green valley a grassland a savanna
Africa Sumbawa

—stop
(stay still)
a bullet shoots through the head
or a heart?

—study anatomy!

—it's all in your head
and they say
33 is just the right age to become a man

—i get it

Mikael Johani

—now it's time
to get off the swing
put on a tie
a pair of bespoke brogues

—there's no such thing
as life sans autopsy
a slaughter
followed by a feast
around a bonfire
wiping red and blackened hands
on linen pants

—no!
life is filled with post-mortem
everything
splitting of assets
who paid for that holiday in Bali
who hesitated to go
whose love was truer?

—better get used to it
i'm getting used to it
appeal
to the Supreme Court of Love and Justice
with you as
the Chief Justice
Judge I
Judge II
Prosecutor
Defense lawyer

—me, i'm the offender
sat on a rattan-backed chair

—on tomorrow's first pages
you'll see photos of my sweaty back

—keep away from crooks

—their crookedness is contagious!

—Honourable Panel of Judges
have mercy
i know not
what i have done
this is not an excuse
not an alibi
this is an appeal for
Your clemency
for i am human
and i need to be loved

—if only life is
as sentimental as i imagine it to be!

—now, remember,
write this down
a cheap notebook will do
does the cover say "goed kwaliteit"?
sit in Popi's
a tiny cafe in Oud Gondangdia
watch the Bogor-bound train

Mikael Johani

cross the moon
arms flailing
out of its open doors
life should feel like this
happily ever after
4eva

—put your Selected Poems
of WCW back in your bag
keep its flap open
this is just a symbolic gesture
you can recite
off the top of your head
The Widow's Lament in Springtime
all the lines from
Journey to Love
(how sweet is
the epigraph:
"For My Wife"
—"the whole process is a lie"!—
this whole poem is a lie

(—unless, as you always do in this city,
you leave a home in complete ruin
and then come back to rebuild it again)

BILANG DENGAN BUNGA

Anya Rompas

translated by Mikael Johani

[editors note: This poem was translated by Anya Rompas' husband, Mikael Johani from the original Indonesian.]

bunga bunga tumbuh menjadi semak belukar di antara gigimu
menjalar menyelubungi kepala melingkari leher dan perlahan
merayap membungkusmu sampai ke ujung jari jari tangan
kakimu merampas segala yang istimewa dari tubuhmu —
kau tak lagi memandangnya sebagai rumah tetapi kerang-
keng ke mana pun kau pergi
ke mana pun kau berlari
ke sudut sudut kantor
ke lorong lorong supermarket
ke jembatan jembatan penyeberangan
kau
terus mendengar bunyi jeruji
berdentang berdentang
dentang dentang
berdentang
tang tang tang

berguncang guncang kerangkengmu guncang guncang
kerangkengmu guncang hidupmu
kepalamu
tang tang tang
bunga bunga terus tumbuh kini beraneka bentuk beraneka
warna akar akarnya menyeruak dari lubang telinga lubang
hidung lubang kemaluanmu mengangkat kuku kuku kaki dan
tanganmu menenggelamkan bola matamu sampai kau tak
yakin lagi apakah mereka benar benar tumbuh dari tubuhmu
atau merangsek ke dalamnya
tak ada lagi bedanya sesungguhnya
kau telah kehilangan atau kau telah menghilang
(kalau mereka bilang) semua ini bukan milikmu bukan peng-
etahuanmu bukan karyamu bukan dirimu

**

flowers grew into bushes
vines between your teeth
snaked around your head your neck slowly creeped around
your body
the tips of your fingers your toes
robbed your body of its magnificence —
you no longer thought of your body as a home you thought of
it as a cell that followed you wherever you went
wherever you ran to
the corner of an office
the aisles in the supermarket the pedestrian bridges
you
keep hearing the rattle of the bars
clang
clang
clang

clang
clang
clang clang clang
your cell clang clang clang clang clang clang the cell that was
your life
your head

clang clang clang
flowers kept growing flowers of many shapes of many colours flower roots kept sprouting out of your ears out of your
nostrils out of your cunt rooting out the nails on your toes on
your fingers digging into your eyeballs until you were not so
sure anymore were they growing out of your body or advanc-
ing against it
there was no difference anymore
between missing a thing and disappearing
(when they said) all this was not yours not your knowledge
not
your art not you

FIRM GROUND

Kasim Mohammed

The man on the screen looks like Harun's dad. Bald, sides of his head closely shaven, dark around his brown eyes, stomach pushing against the threads of his clothes, almost-purple lips against his pale skin, somewhere in between brown and white.

He is holding a piece of paper in his hands and he gestures to the words on it, tracing them with his finger, reading them out loud:

"It's okay to be gay. You can have two mummies. You can have two daddies. You can be a girl in a boy's body. You can be a boy in a girl's body."

The camera cuts to his face, and he is surrounded by other men, one of them is wearing white salwar kameez, a white topi on his head, the kind of costume Harun wears to Jummah every week, to kneel amongst his brothers, to pray to Allah.

"This is not acceptable in Islam. God created man and then he created woman for man's pleasure and for his companionship. He did not create man for man," he continues, his accent, tone and cadence the very same Harun hears in the corner shop where he goes to buy bread, hand extended out for salaam, stroking the head of the cat before he leaves.

The camera pans over the crowd, where there are women standing, some of them wrapped in scarves, signs in their hands, cardboard held up high, giant words painted onto it: MY CHILD MY CHOICE.

The clip is part of a segment shown on the news, and Harun sits in his living room as it airs, his father and mother on the other side of the room, his father on his phone, scrolling endlessly on Facebook, barely paying attention to what is happening, his mother captivated by it.

The first time Harun heard about this scandal, he was at work, sitting at his desk, writing copy for a car company, when Aaron, the only other non-white guy at work, a black guy, a new starter, his head closely-shaved, his face delicate in a way that could only be described as pretty, his body solid from the time he spends at the gym, his shirt tight against it in a way that he wants it to, came up to him.

"Heard about this school?" he asked.

Harun shook his head, and so Aaron told him, all about how this white gay teacher had started to teach LGBTQ+ lessons at a Muslim school, and Harun listened, wondering why the name felt so familiar to him, and it was only when he searched for it, found videos and tweets, located it on a map, that he realised it was down the street from where he lived.

That day, he had dreaded going home, because he knew that his mother would want to talk about it, and Harun didn't have anything to add to the conversation. Or, at least, he didn't have anything to add to it that she would want to hear.

"It's just wrong," she says, and she turns the volume on the TV down, turning to Harun, who looks up from his phone, pretending not to have heard the news, pretending not to have seen the images on screen. "This school stuff. It's wrong."

"Oh," he says. "Is that still going on?"

"It's going to go on for as long as we need it to. You know

they haven't stopped, right?"

"Stopped protesting?"

"No, they haven't stopped teaching it. They say that this programme that this teacher came up with is going to continue in the schools."

"And the parents have the right to take their children out of it, right?"

"Which they have," she says, and Harun looks back at the screen, sees the children standing outside of the school, holding up signs, repeating what their parents are saying, and he wonders how many of them even know what they're there for, wonders how many of them even know what they're saying, how many of them even care.

"So then what's the issue?"

"Harun," she says, and she says it the same way she says his name when he reaches into the pile of pakoreh that she has made for later, the same way she says his name when he tells her he's going to be out late and she has made food, the same way she says his name when he lets her down. "It's not about that. It's about the fact that they never told the parents before they started teaching the children. It's about how they're now painting us as these backwards people who don't care about the LGBTQ+ community."

"But they don't," Harun says. "Those people are saying that they don't want their children even knowing about it."

"Because they're too young. These are children, six, seven years old. They don't need to know about gay people and what they do. Like they're talking all this talk about freedom of speech but where is our freedom of speech? Where is the protection of people who have a religion?"

Harun bites his tongue. "I don't know, Mum."

"I don't know," she says, repeating his words, and she sounds so melancholic, so hollow.

Harun goes back to his phone, idly scrolling through Twitter, hoping that he can see something to distract him, but the words blur past him, none of them make sense, and all he can hear is the man that looks like his father.

It comes up again at work the next day. Aaron walks over to his desk, shows him a video on his phone of a group of queer Muslims talking about the issue. Harun watches it, Aaron leaning over him, arm pressed on his shoulder, holding the phone, and he listens to each one of them talk about what it means to them to be queer and Muslim, how they exist in the world, how the binary simplicity that people seem to think of as reality, that queerness and Islam are at odds with one another, isn't the truth, and Harun finds a knot in his stomach, his throat closing up with every second that passes.

"What do you think?" Aaron asks when the video is over.

"What do I think?" Harun says.

"Well, yeah. You're Muslim, right?" Harun nods. "So you must have an opinion?"

Harun looks at him, shrugs his shoulders. "I think that I probably need to read a lot more about it before I say anything."

Aaron half-laughs. "That's fair enough."

And then he leaves and Harun watches him go, turns back to his computer, starts typing, but finds that he can't think about anything else but that video, of Aaron leaning over his shoulder showing it to him, and he feels a rush of fire race through him, blood pounding, cheeks red.

He spends the rest of his day working and when the time comes to go home, he packs his things, slings his bag over his shoulder, and finds Aaron waiting for him when he turns around. "What's up?" he says, stilling the tremor in his voice.

"I know you don't drink but do you want to go out tonight?" Aaron asks. Harun's stomach flips. "It's okay if you're busy. I just thought..."

"I have a family thing tonight," Harun says, lying because he doesn't know how else to react. The words just fall out of his mouth. "Dinner with my parents." He smiles apologetically. "But maybe next time?"

"Yeah, sure," Aaron says, and he steps out of the way and Harun gives him a small smile as he walks past him, heading out of the office, and he doesn't look back as he walks down the hallway, down the stairs, out of the building, and when the cool air hits him, he realises that he's been holding his breath this entire time, and he lets it out, this big whoosh, and he walks to his bus stop, and it's only when the bus comes, when he sits, that he realises he left his headphones at work.

That night, he sits at the table with his parents, eating the chicken he helped his mother make when he came home from work, cutting the onions alongside her, letting the chicken boil, pink turning white, the smell of spices lingering in the air.

"Harun, do you remember Layla?" his mother asks, and he pauses, roti half-way to his mouth, and he shakes his head, even though he does. "She's Salma's daughter. Remember? A year younger than you, went to university to become a dentist, just finished? She works now, passed her work placement just a few months ago."

"That's cool," Harun says, and he looks down at his plate, trying to hide the shame that floods his cheeks, the embarrassment.

"Well, her mother phoned the other day. We were just talking about things and she asked about you."

"Oh?" he says, not looking up.

"Yeah, and I told her you had a job, a good job, and you were with us still. Not like those other boys you hear about, the ones who leave their parents as soon as they can." She laughs and he looks up at her, sees her staring right at him, her eyes pointed.

"I think what your mother is trying to get at," his father says, and Harun looks at him, "is that Layla is single and looking to get married."

His mother gives his father a look and then turns back to Harun. "Okay, yes. Layla is looking to settle down. She's finished her degree, she has a job. She wants to get married to someone good, have a few kids. You know, build a life for herself."

"And you want me to marry her?" Harun asks. He suddenly doesn't feel so hungry anymore.

"Well, only if you want to. We just want to know if you'll meet her," his father says. "She's a good girl. And you remember her. You met her at that wedding we went to last summer. Who was it?"

"Oh, Zakira, right?" his mother says.

And Harun is back there, dressed in a sherwani, which feels too extravagant for him to wear to a wedding where he barely knows the people, but his mother had insisted, told him he looked good in it, and it's only when she introduces him to Layla that he realises why she had insisted, and he smiles at Layla, knowing exactly what his mother is doing, and Layla smiles back, and she's pretty in a non-threatening way, and they speak a little, Layla finishing her degree, Harun just starting his job, and then they are gone and he puts her to the back of his mind.

"Zakira," Harun says, tasting the name in his mouth.

"We're just saying," his mother says, and he looks at her, sees her eyes, big and brown, filled with concern, "maybe it's time you started thinking about marriage. You're older than we were when we got married."

"I think everyone is older than you were when you got married."

"Different times," his father says.

"Is there anyone?" his mother asks.

Harun shifts where he sits a little, and he feels like a child again, being asked if he did something wrong. "No," he says, and he feels this punch to his gut, like he has let them down, like he has somehow disappointed them, and he looks down at his food so he doesn't have to see his mother's eyes.

They don't push the issue further and Harun lies in bed that night, awake, thinking of how they asked him every year of university if he had found someone, his mother telling him to join the Asian society, to make friends, to find his people, how he always told her that he had joined the Asian society but they didn't do much even though he hadn't because he found it both intimidating and embarrassing, how he stayed by himself most of the time, not going to clubs and turning down invitations, how he spent the three years there watching people touch one another, press their bodies close, fingertips tracing the canvas of one another, and staying away from it all.

His parents don't bring Layla up again but Harun can't stop thinking about her, looking her up on Facebook, her profile private, locked away, but her profile picture open, and he stares at it, at how blandly attractive she is, how there is nothing wrong with her face but he feels nothing for it, and he finds himself thinking about marrying her, what it might be like to bring her into his parents' home, what it might be like to live with her, to maybe own a house one day, to have children, to live the kind of life that his parents want...

"Pretty," Aaron says, and Harun almost falls out of his chair in his rush to close the window, turning around to block his screen.

"She's no one," he says, and he knows he says it like he has everything to hide, and he can see Aaron's eyes shift a little.

"No one," Aaron says, and he smiles as if he can see right into Harun's mind, figure out exactly who Layla is. "Could you help me with something?"

"Yeah, sure," Harun says, standing from his desk, reaching to lock his computer, the screen fading to black. "What is it?"

"Well," Aaron says, and he starts walking to his desk, which is not far but not close, and Harun feels this odd shifting in his stomach, this back and forth, like someone is rolling a heavy ball around inside him. "I'm trying to figure out this SEO stuff." He offers his chair to Harun, who takes it, trying not to think about Aaron sitting right where he is. "So," Aaron says, leaning over him, moving the mouse around, "I have this copy. Client has signed off on it and everything. But I'm just trying to figure this bit out."

"Ah," Harun says, and he reaches for the mouse just as Aaron moves his hand back, fingers sliding over one another, the soft brush of skin meeting skin. "Once you get the hang of it, it's easy. You just put the keywords in, what you think is best to find the people searching for these things. So this copy is about holidays, so you just type in holidays. But try to be more specific, and it's always good to think of the opposite."

"The opposite?" Aaron asks, head hovering somewhere close by Harun's right ear.

"Yeah, so it's good to think about offensive words. So like say if you were writing copy about a certain type of car, it's good to then use a competitor's name to get people redirected here. So if they type in that car's name, they'll see this instead."

"Isn't that lying?"

Harun turns to him, finds himself looking right at Aaron, inches apart. "Not really," he says, and he pushes himself back a little, chair moving, wheels scratching on the carpet. "There's some other stuff you can do too..."

"Did you think about that drink?" Aaron asks.

"Drink?" Harun says, and he feels blood rush to his face.

"Well, not an alcoholic drink. But maybe just some food. I don't really know anyone around here so..."

"Yeah," Harun says, interrupting Aaron. "I can do tonight."

Aaron smiles, this gradual lightening of his face, as though a light has been turned up, dial turned. "Yeah?" he asks.

Layla's face hovers before Harun's eyes and he nods. "Yeah, I think that should be fine."

"Okay," Aaron says, and he looks back at the screen and Harun follows, half a second later, his eyes lingering on the shape of Aaron's face, the line of his jaw.

When five comes around, Harun sits at his desk, restless, looking at the time in the bottom right hand corner of his screen, feeling almost sick. Part of him wants to leave, go home, eat with his parents, but he takes a breath, deep, fills his lungs with it, stills himself.

"Ready?" he hears, and he stands, finding Aaron behind him, an easy smile on his lips.

"Ready," Harun says, and he walks out, alongside Aaron, and a little voice in his head asks him what he's doing, and he quietens it, tells it to be silent, but it's hard not to wonder what his plan is here.

"So I think there's this really nice place, new I think, Mexican. You don't mind Mexican right?" Aaron asks as they stand waiting for the lift to arrive.

"No, I don't," Harun says. "It just has to be…"

"Halal?" Aaron asks. "I already checked. They are."

Harun feels a little thrill in his chest and he wants to say something, to thank Aaron of thinking of him like that, but the lift beeps as it arrives, and they step into the metal box.

"So how long have you worked here?"

"Just over a year," Harun says.

"Oh," Aaron says.

"Oh?"

"I thought you had just joined too," Aaron says. "That's why I thought maybe you wouldn't mind hanging out."

"You thought I had just joined," Harun says, and he feels like running away.

"I just… It doesn't matter," Aaron says, and Harun lets the conversation die, and when the doors open, he almost says he's changed his mind, that he wants to go home, that he's forgotten it's someone's birthday, but he doesn't, so they walk out together, into the open world.

They are silent for a while, Harun not sure where to look, what to say.

"Thanks for today," Aaron says, after what feels like an

infinity of nothing. "I really appreciate it."

"It's cool," Harun says. "I know what it feels like to be new at a job."

"Thank you anyway."

It feels like Harun's chest is going to explode. "So why copywriting?" he asks.

"Ah," Aaron says with a chuckle. "You sound just like my dad."

"Oh?"

"Yeah. I did a degree in English, masters in Creative Writing, because I wanted to be a writer."

"Wanted?"

Aaron sucks in air between his teeth. "Well, it's not really the easiest thing to break into."

"Well, no, but you can't just give up."

"Oh, this isn't me giving up. It's just me selling out for a corporate job, at a desk every day, five days a week, so I can earn enough money to actually spend time writing." He pauses for a second. "Not that I mean..."

"Oh, don't worry," Harun says. "I'm not doing this because it's the dream job. I just didn't know what else I wanted to do with my English degree."

"You too?"

"Oh, yeah. And my dad still doesn't get it. He doesn't know why I studied the language I speak, even though I tried to tell him that it's not the language, it's more..."

"The art," Aaron says.

"The art," Harun repeats.

"Like I could have done medicine or law or something. I don't know if I would have been smart enough for it but I definitely could have tried. But I never wanted to do that.

Like being a doctor is important and you save lives, but art is important too, right? It's how we see the world, how we make sense of things."

"My granddad always used to say that stories are the way we share ourselves with each other," Harun says, his grandfather's voice in his head.

"That's a pretty nice way of seeing the world."

"He always had a pretty nice way of seeing the world," Harun says, and he feels a slight emptiness inside his chest.

They stay silent for a moment, and it doesn't feel as though the silence is awkward, uncomfortable.

Suddenly, Aaron stops walking and Harun does too, the two of them facing each other, and Aaron nods to behind Harun. "We're here," he says, and Harun turns, finds himself facing a restaurant he has never heard of before.

They step in, and the evening passes before Harun like a blink, neither of them somehow able to stop talking, going from family to university, to the books they've read, to Aaron's writing, something he is somehow both confident and insecure about, the rejections he's received, Harun's own writing, the little things he does, Aaron telling him to do more, both of them telling the other they want to read what they've written, and when it all comes to an end, standing at the end of a road, having to split, Harun reaches out his hand and Aaron laughs, pushes it away, holds Harun tight against him, and Harun puts his arms around him, feels the strength of his body, closes his eyes, leans into him, and for a moment, it feels like the world has fallen away from under his feet and there is nothing to fear.

The weekend comes quickly, and Harun goes with his parents to his grandmother's house, who lives by herself, despite his mother repeatedly asking her to live with them, refusing to become dependent on other people. His aunt and uncle are there too, and when Harun and his parents arrive, they are already talking in the living room.

"But you see what's happening here, right?" his aunt says as Harun takes his shoes off in the hallway. "On one hand you have the LGBTQ+ community, with its liberal language, who are able to speak to the media, the majority white media don't forget, about these issues in a way that they respond to. And on the other hand, you have the brown Muslims, a disenfranchised group of people who have never felt understood by the discourse in the country, who don't have access to that language, who don't speak it, who don't recognise it, and because of that, they're being labelled backwards. It's rampant Islamophobia. It's racism, it's prejudice. Where is the freedom of religious rights here? Where is the respect given to these parents?"

The words echo in his chest as he steps through, heart heavy, and they turn to him, aunt and uncle, both single, both without children, aunt divorced, uncle never married.

"Welcome, welcome," his uncle says, and he spreads his arms wide. "She's on one again." A grin on his face.

"I'm not on one. I'm just saying, there are things to think about here. You agree, right?" she asks, looking at Harun's mother, bypassing any kind of welcome.

"Is this about the school?" His aunt nods. "It came up at work again the other day."

"Oh yeah?" his aunt asks.

"Well, we were all in the teachers' room with our lunches and then someone started talking about it, how they understood why the parents were so against it, because there had been no consultation at all, and then it just went off. I tried to say something but everyone was just loud and thought their opinion was the one that mattered so I just stopped saying anything," Harun's mum says.

"And that's the problem too," his aunt says. "People are so loud and that's what people respond to. You have to be so loud to get anyone to hear you. But then you get told that you're being too loud and that you're being aggressive. It all just comes down to politics and talking and language and the way you look and the way you speak and the way you present yourself to the world. No one is saying anything to the Christian schools or the Jewish schools who don't want this stuff taught in their classrooms. It's all about us."

Harun watches her as she talks and he wonders why someone with no children is so affronted by this, someone who doesn't know anyone with children at the school, and he wonders why any of them are talking about it when it doesn't directly affect them, and he wonders why he can't think of anything to say, why this issue makes his throat clam up, why it makes him forget all language, why words come so hard to him.

"What do you think, Harun?" He looks up, sees his uncle looking at him. "As the youngest person in the room?"

"Me?" Harun says, and he feels stuck, frozen, like a light has just been cast on him and he can't think of anything to say.

"Yes, you. You're the closest one to school here. How would you feel about it if you were there again?"

Harun looks from uncle to aunt, from aunt to mother, from mother to uncle, and he feels shaky, breath trapped in his chest. "I don't know," he says. "I guess it depends."

"Depends on what? It's against Islam," his aunt says.

"I know…"

"And they didn't consult the parents at all. They didn't say anything. And you can't deny that there's an air of racism here, of Islamophobia."

"I'm not saying…"

"It's all down to the way you present yourself. If you don't look like them, they're not going to listen to you. They don't want to listen to us. Look everywhere. Politics is crumbling. Everyone is siloed off into their own little groups. And we're not part of a group that is listened to. They actively hate us, even though we give them everything we have. We pay our taxes, we work in their economy, and yet new policies come up that are targeting us, every day something is on the news about how we don't deserve our humanity, our rights…"

Her voice fades out for Harun. All he can hear is his heartbeat, and he wants to close his eyes, clamp his hands over his ears, be still, not listen to anything.

He sits opposite Aaron in the same place as the one they went to before, menu propped up in front of him. "So I didn't say anything."

"Do you wish that you did?" Aaron asks.

Harun looks at the menu, doesn't meet Aaron's eyes. "I wish they would stop talking to me about it."

When he doesn't say anything else, Aaron asks, "Why?"

"Because I think…" He bites his tongue, swallows his words. "Because I think that we have different ideas about the world. I just want everyone to get along. And if that means teaching children that all kinds of different people exist in the world, then I'm all for that."

"I don't think there's anything wrong with that."

"Neither do I."

"But if that's what you believe, then you have to stand for that, right? If you don't stand for something, you'll fall for anything."

"Profound," Harun says.

"I'm just saying," Aaron says, and Harun lifts his eyes, looks at him, "if that's how you feel, you have to be open about it."

Harun looks back at the menu, ignoring the fluttering in his stomach, trying to find something to eat, but suddenly, the words are blurred and his head is pounding and he feels faint.

"Just know where you stand, that's all. It makes it easier to defend yourself," Aaron says.

And so the evening whirls past them again, and even as Harun sits there in the booth with him, after spending all day at work with him, small jokes thrown Harun's way on Slack, eating together at lunch, he finds that he is missing Aaron even as he is talking to him, some kind of mourning for the future, when Aaron is gone and he is making his way home again, and he sits in it, this weird blend of missing Aaron and enjoying his company all at the same time, and when they walk together, away from the food, towards their solo journeys home, he takes a half-beat longer with each step, dragging out every second.

They stand where they split into two and Harun is waiting for Aaron to say something, to hug him like last time, and as he thinks about the way Aaron's body felt, how it fit into him, he feels this rush of something in the middle of his chest and he feels light, so light it's almost painful.

"You know, when I came out to my dad, he didn't speak to me for a few weeks," Aaron says. His voice is soft, his words slow. "I was fifteen, a year after my mum died, and there we were, sitting in this house, not knowing how to be around each other. She'd always been the bridge between us, bringing us together, and without her, I didn't understand the layout of the house anymore. It felt like someone had come to us in the middle of the night, rearranged everything, and me and Dad, we were just stumbling in the darkness, trying to find our way out. When he stopped talking to me, it actually felt easier. Because then I didn't have to make the effort. I could just pretend that we were nothing to each other. But it wore on me. I started hating him. I started hating myself. So I pushed him to talk to me, forced him to."

Aaron's voice doesn't shake, is strong and calm and solid, and Harun wants to fall into it, let it wrap around him. "Do you talk to him now?" he asks.

"A little," Aaron says. "I don't think we were ever going to be good to one another, not the way I wish we were, but we have something. But it took a lot of time. We talked and talked and talked. He asked me if Mum knew before she died and I told him I guess she must have because we spent so much time together, and he told me he had no idea because I didn't talk gay or act gay or whatever. And I told him I guess gay people are as different as straight people, right? We're all individuals. But do you know what made all of it easier? Knowing where I stood, where I was, where I wanted to be."

Harun looks at him, not saying anything, because he doesn't have anything to say, and he watches as Aaron's eyes flick away from his for a moment, only to come back.

"Just know who you are," he says. "It makes everything easier to deal with."

And then he moves to Harun, holding him again, arms

wrapped around him, and Harun leans into him, head slotted perfectly into the space between shoulder and head, like someone has carved out that space for him, and he holds Aaron tight, and if he could take this feeling and bottle it somehow, he would, taking it out whenever he feels that the world is against him and know that he is safe here, in this person's arms, and when Aaron pulls back, he doesn't pull back the entire way, he stays close to him, so little distance between them, and there is something said between them that doesn't require words, and Aaron moves, presses his lips against Harun's, so soft, so light, and Harun feels like he is about to throw up, his stomach twitching and twisting, and yet it feels right, like something of him has been found, and his eyes close without being told to, and he doesn't move, is frozen, almost delirious with ecstasy.

They move apart after what feels like a lifetime and Harun opens his eyes, sees that same grin, and he smiles too, stepping back, a small chuckle coming out of his mouth, and he doesn't know if he should feel embarrassed or elated.

"Sorry," Aaron says.

Harun shakes his head. "Don't," he says. "That was..." And he stops because he doesn't know how to quantify that, words failing him.

"Good?" Aaron asks.

"Good," Harun says.

And so they stand there, looking at one another, and for the first time in forever, Harun's mind is quiet, there is so very little noise up there, and Aaron tells him he'll see him at work and Harun says he will too, and he watches as Aaron walks away and he does too, and as he waits for his bus, he thinks about where his feet are, never before have they been planted on such firm ground, and his entire body feels so sensitive, every atom brushing against his skin electrifying, and too many things start to make sense to him and he wants to laugh, to scream, to shout, and he does none of those things, just stands there and waits, and he remembers the feeling of being kissed, runs fingers over his lips, and he bottles that feeling up, puts it to the back of his mind, safe and secure, to take out when it feels like the entire world is against him.

Because at least now, he knows where he stands.

MIRACLE

Jen Calleja

On the shuttle from Fiumicino Airport to Termini, I start feeling small and anxious. After a brief email exchange, the Swiss author whose novel I'm currently translating has invited me to come and spend six days and five nights with her in Rome, where she is in residence for ten months – so here I am. I project various possible worst-case scenarios, including her disappointment in me and/or the translation, misunderstandings, awkward silences, and ultimate rejection resulting in evenings spent eating alone in my room (wherever this will be, I haven't asked a lot of questions) onto the passing view of apartment blocks.

I'm in Italy to spend long periods of time with not only a stranger, but a stranger who is relying on me. Will she find me strange, boring, childish, unprofessional?

I spot her wearing a bright red jacket where we had agreed to meet, between two gilded Christmas trees, and I warm my face up to smile so I can give a positive first impression. I don't want her to take one look at me and think: I see brooding, self-conscious days before me.

I apologise that she has been expecting me for nearly an hour already because I hadn't made the earlier train, and she gives a little shrug and a smile and says that it was no trouble at all. This tiny gesture dissolves all my circular predictions. A more relaxing and familiar passing of time together comes into focus in my mind's eye.

After a short walk through the already darkening streets flooding with the rush of the end of the working day, we arrive at what looks like a Beverly Hills mansion or an amusement park ride or an immersive installation. A palatial house, surrounded by a high stone wall. Through the automatic gates I can see a man-made, arched faux-rock grotto, which shelters three pools of koi carp.

The house seems to float above and slightly back from this rocky cliff-esque creation. It has a very large, mesmerising, magical purple neon sign that reads

MIRACLE

on the front of it, which is splashing the palm trees around it with violet light. I imagine a mysterious song beginning to play in the distance. Later I'll learn that hidden speakers play birdsong to scare off the green parakeets here in the grounds of the house.

She shows me around the walled grounds of the Villa Maraini, now the Swiss Institute in Rome. Private gardens, with a fountain, and cockatoos in a cage. Lemon, orange and grapefruit trees covered in cheerful fruit. There are many entrance-exits to the institute. If you come in the front, you walk via the reception down a long mirrored corridor where you greet the bust of the architect, Otto Maraini, before getting into the wooden lift.

My room has the highest ceiling I've ever seen. The twin single beds have bright yellow duvets that reflect against the

walls, just as the zingy purple MIRACLE reflects on the building opposite the right-hand window. The en-suite has white
and yellow tiles.

* * *

I don't personally believe in fate or mysticism, but coinci-
dences, connections, repetitions and déjà vu have always
guided my life with their reassuring signs. I know I'm sus-
ceptible to them, but often they surprise me, as if they really
are naturally occurring. Some are clear, others more subtle.
For instance, I have a one-year-old cat, she is called Ludo
(Ludovica). The street where the institute is located is called
via Ludovisi, after the creator of the villa turned museum in
the nearby park, Ludovico Ludovisi. It feels like the trip's
been signed off on when I discover this.

When something amazing, almost miraculous happens,
it's thrilling because it seems to be the manifestation of the
impossible, even if it can often be logically explained away.
Sometimes, however, it does feel like it would have always
been unattainable until that very moment.

Almost a year to the day before standing in the driveway
of the Istituto Svizzero in Rome, I was at a salon being held by
the Swiss-German author Ulrike Ulrich in Zurich while writ-
er-in-residence with her writers' collective, telling the assembled members in the warm flat that I was reading a book I
felt a strong connection with, a book that was like a waking
dream or nightmare that I couldn't get off my mind. It was
Michelle Steinbeck's *Mein Vater war ein Mann an Land und
im Wasser ein Walfisch* (*My Father was a Man on Land and
a Whale in the Water*). A surreal story of a young woman

who accidentally murders a child and goes on an adventure to bring it to her father in a suitcase is one way of describing it, and now, through a strange series of events (being entranced by the cover, being given the book by a friend, a chance tip-off), I was translating it, and it had brought me to Rome.

And even before all of this, ten years before being in Zurich working on my own novel, I would have been in the first few months of university in London, the first person in my family to go into higher education – overwhelmed, shy, reclusive, mildly traumatised and broken-hearted after my year spent living mostly alone in Munich (my German: still terrible) and starting to write my first complete stories and poems and personal essays to submit to the university magazine.

And five years before Munich? Starting my first relationship, believing that I would never leave my hometown. At some point that year I read a short story my best friend had written, and I was confused and in awe as I devoured it in her bedroom with her sitting next to me – *do regular people write stories, poems, books, not just read them?*

Four long years before abruptly reconnecting with the idea of writing while in my friend's room, I was excused from going to school assemblies to write stories with a couple of other pupils. Whether it was because I had shown talent, or because things were complicated at home again, I don't remember. I think this was also around the time I wet myself in a supermarket car park because I was, perhaps, too passive and nervous, or it just hadn't occurred to me to ask my parents if I could go to the bathroom while they loaded up the car with shopping.

And, to do the unthinkable? Go back a further five years? I was a serious, odd, practically silent child. 'An old head on young shoulders', my first school report would read.

My 4-year old, 9-year-old, 13-year-old, 18-year-old, 19-year-old and even 29-year-old selves would never have anticipated or even at that point really desired this private, perhaps wholly minor and ordinary miracle to ever happen, but at 30 (and, as of a week ago, 31), I'm glad that I never saw this coming, rather than it feeling like something I had just simply been waiting for, something I've always been destined to do. At what point in my life did an experience like this, being in Rome with Michelle, come to be on the cards?

After I had been confirmed to translate her book, I learned from Michelle that the year previous to my six-week stay in the little attic room in Zurich, she had sat at the same desk in the same room writing this book, our book, while between flats. We had both written our books in the same place. I had brought her book with me and it had been on the bedside table during my time there.

There's a framed poem by the German poet Durs Grünbein about this institute in the corridor a couple of floors down from our rooms. He too had been a resident here. I had written my master's dissertation on Michael Hofmann's English translations of Grünbein's poetry five years ago. *Ja, ich war hier!'* – *Yes, I was here!* is scrawled above his signature, all of it written in red-orange colouring pencil or crayon, a bold choice, as if he were as stoked to be here as I was. But I believe it's also a reference to a line in one of his poems on the aftermath of the bombing of Dresden: *'du bist nicht dabei gewesen' (you weren't there)*, itself a reference to the criticism he received for witnessing something in his poetry that he didn't experience himself. There are unspoken rules around this kind of thing.

The day before arriving in Rome, I had given a talk at the

university where I'd done my master's about my career as a literary translator since graduating, opening with the anecdote that in one of our lectures we were discouraged from trying to become translators of literature because it was too difficult, practically impossible.

An unforeseen, glorious return.

The good and bad things that have happened have led to this defining moment; a unique constellation of events has brought me here, in spite of certain obstacles and false starts.

***

Foucault said: 'Do not ask me who I am and do not ask me to remain the same'. Don't define me, and don't expect me to remain fixed. A translated line might say this too. (Is this line also a translation? One possible translation of the line? It is in any/every case a translation from Foucault's undulating mind into the outside.)

We ask so much of translated lines:

But what exactly are you?

Trust me, relax, just enjoy our time together, and take my word that I'm the same as the original.

But did you keep all the words? What do you mean you could appear in a different guise?

Not only am I nothing like the original, but I could appear as a whole array of nothing-like-the-originals.

***

We nonchalantly create a routine for ourselves. We meet on the landing at 9/9.30/10 (neither of us is a morning person) and trot down the stairs, me trailing her, to go and have a coffee and a croissant-like pastry, due cappuccini e due cornetti. Or un cornetto – from one morning to the next Michelle wants or doesn't want one depending on how she feels in the decisive moment, or on how the pastries look.

Then we go back and print a chapter of my translation in the beautiful, underused, partially subterranean library, with lemons and oranges hanging outside the window, and then go all the way up to Michelle's atelier in the roof with a pot of green tea for her and black tea for me. The room has three porthole windows, and a ridiculously oversized wooden desk.

We go through the opening chapter first, which had sealed the deal for me to be the translator, along with my apparent enthusiasm.

Enthusiasm as part of a translation practice.

Working together is relaxed, easy, intense, serious, jokey, meticulous.

We discuss words, word orders, single sentences, for hours.

The subsequent chapters we dissect are not final drafts – they include the multiple word and line choices I keep until I do my second draft. I want to see what choices Michelle would make in English, though I get the final say, she confirms:

a barrage of abuse / a wave of insults

steam roller / lawn roller

survey one another / look each other up and down

you're a damn liar / you're a lying so-and-so / you're lying left, right and centre

happy are the little children / ignorance is bliss

fashioned / constructed / pieced together / thrown together / assembled

113

kid / child (and should we consider Kid with a capital K? Because it's not wholly a kid, it's also both dead and undead, but not a zombie, but also a metaphor, but also a child, and in German you can just have 'das Kind' that has that archetypal power you lose in the English, but then would it just become a metaphor, an archetype?)

Mastiffs / Great Danes (and can you really claim a Great Dane is the size of a calf? I'll check…

Image: 'Baby Calf Rescued From Slaughterhouse Thinks He's A D…':

'What they didn't expect to happen, was that their Great Dane had actually taken up the role of the calf's mother! The Dane's name is Leonidas, and together…')

Google Image Searching 'Great Dane and Calf' as translation research.

She especially loved the word peculiar.

Anything funny, weird or strange we come across during our time in Rome we declare *peculiar*.

Though we only work in the morning/early afternoon and one evening, the book remains mapped onto my experience of Rome. I see the suitcase (carrying the Kid) on the pavement, I see the whole fish (that the Father's pregnant wife loves to eat pickled) lying in the street. My window with palms thrashing about in a storm (like the view where the strange Artists live at sea) distracts and transports me.

***

Michelle is wonderful in restaurants.

She strides in smiling, laughing at the waiter's quips I don't understand, patiently translates everything on the menu for me and is still happy to choose and confidently order, asking questions.

We go to a very nice restaurant near the institute. As we're looking at the menu, a woman as part of a couple at the table next to us is complaining about her dish.

'I thought it would have a sauce and be filled with sea-food!' she loudly tells the waiter in English with a Russian accent, prodding a plate of what looks like plain spaghetti.

'That's what I'm going to get,' Michelle says. 'It's *ricci de mare.*'

I look it up: sea urchins.

While we're waiting, we get on to talking about being comparatively young, on being presumed to be middle class because we're writers, and eventually, Me Too.

Everything blurs even further in this moment. Is this two young writers, now friends, having dinner? Is this an author and her translator after a day of work? Is this two young women talking about being patronised, harassed and assaulted? If it is all of the above, what does this mean?

She had written a piece about being assaulted by a col-league at a theatre she was working at when a few of them stayed the night to save going home in torrential rain. When I read the piece online it made me feel connected to her – the author I'm translating has experienced what I have experi-enced.

'Me Too' an important moment, we agree. I personally couldn't muster the energy to do anything public in this moment. It brought a lot of things whooshing back from some other, hidden place, and I felt mute and frozen.

But I tell Michelle.

About the older translator who forcibly kissed me twice at a work meeting in a cafe. About someone who's acted inappropriately at different times when we've been alone or when greeting me at literary events and once even bit me on the mouth. The work meetings where it has become clear that the editor or programme manager or whoever doesn't want to talk about work at all and has decided it's a date.

I won't talk about the music scene here.

But if any of you who have wronged me and feigned respect for me knowing that I looked up to you at the time as peers are reading this, I just want to say in this moment, though it changes every moment: I'm disappointed.

I could have easily said disturbed/exhausted/angry/revengeful.

Dinner as, no, not confessional: as cathartic curse casting.

When Michelle's meal is set down, there is a pungent waft of stagnant pond, and she seems to regret her choice with a screwed-up face. It is a portion of very simple spaghetti, but with two dark blots on the side with some parsley – they look like two thin slivers of liver, or blood clots, or leeches.

Giggling, we dare each other to eat a leech. I go first, and it is like chewing a salty slug that tastes like the bottom of an old fish tank.

When the waiter comes over to see if she's enjoying it, as if to prove the woman's complaint was unfounded, Michelle looks up wide-eyed and says it's 'intenso'. Then we both burst out laughing.

From then on, anything bad we see or discuss we declare *leech*.

Anything good we declare *intenso*.

***

On Sunday and Tuesday morning we don't work.

We spend a few hours on Sunday walking around a market. My feet are like ice, and browsing means squeezing through tiny paths between the stalls. I had forgotten that no matter what tat there is at a market, the fun and the thrill is the treasure you might find.

At the very first stall we both try on the same creamy mohair coat, and I eventually buy it. It's like nothing I would usually wear, and maybe seeing Michelle wear it first imbued it with something that made me want it. Walking around Rome with Michelle feels like I'm inhabiting her and her voice; I feel like I'm in her world.

Wearing the coat feels like dressing up, like I'm someone completely different, which is partly how I feel when I'm out of the country and away from people who know me anyway. I can act differently, be confident, outlandish, even coquettish, because no-one will call me out for being a fraud: someone seeing me in the street is none the wiser about who I am, that is, what the process was that resulted in the version of me I am at this point. Out of context, I can experiment a little.

Playing dress-up as experimental translation of self.

Michelle finds an old framed print of an angularly drawn bird with a wineglass – a poster for an alcohol brand from the 70s. As she walks through the market, people stop her to ask about the print. An old lady says that she used to have a similar one, a young man asks, did you know that brand now sponsors the big literary prize in Italy? An old man working at a stall says, bello, it reminds him of being a boy, and, how much will she sell it for?

117

On Tuesday, my last morning in Rome, Michelle books us a viewing slot at an exquisite art museum, Galleria Borghese, in the nearby park.

I had already walked around the park on Saturday afternoon on my own. In the Pincian Gardens, where the view overlooking Rome and Vatican City is, there are 228 busts depicting famous Italian thinkers, scientists, writers and artists, and only three are women. Of its time, we might say. It made me feel like I was trespassing, which made smirking at them more enjoyable. What must it feel like to be a young girl walking around here? There are a lot of young couples making out on the benches in the incredible light.

The museum gives me a sore neck from looking up at the adorned and painted ceilings. Every look in any direction is too much to take in; my eyes focus on tiny, often whimsical details as a defence mechanism against the onslaught of seeing so much. Cherubs blowing bubbles, a badly painted baby. Room after room of marble sculptures and paintings and hand-painted wallpapers and tiled fireplaces and a whole room of Popes. How is two hours enough?

I enter one of the larger rooms.

The central piece is a version of the same sculpture I've seen many times before at the Victoria and Albert Museum in London. The version in Rome, like much of what is in this museum, is by Bernini. While writing this piece, I find out that the other, poorer quality sculpture in London is possibly by an artist called de' Rossi, but is more likely by an artist called Peri.

The sculpture before me has the title *Ratto di Proserpina*, and though I don't speak Italian, I remember what the title of the sculpture is in London—*The Rape of Proserpina*. I remember my double take – this white marble sculpture of a man gracefully heaving a woman into the air is called *The Rape...*? The English translation given underneath the Italian title in Rome—and, I discover online, the new title of the sculpture at the V&A—is just *Pluto & Proserpina*.

Translation as half-arsed substitute for not worshipping the depiction of violence against women, imaginary or otherwise.

Yes, it meant *something different then*, 'to be carried off' as in 'stolen from one man by another/lowered in value for exchange' as much as the simpler meaning we still have today. While researching this, I find there's a term and accompanying body of work for this kind of unsettling depiction: 'heroic rape', where the act of violence is romanticised, sanitised.

Hit by Cupid's arrow/not responsible for his natural urges, Pluto/Hades falls in love/kidnaps/takes by force/assaults Proserpina/Persephone and takes her to the underworld/and does who knows what else, is how the myth goes.

Myths from every age and era dictate our contemporary expectations of ourselves and others.

'Ancient myths' is another term for 'present frameworks of reality'.

The text accompanying the sculpture is leading, to say the least:

'portraying a woman trying to escape from a lover'

'succumbing to the god's strength'

'represents an admirable contrast between tenderness and cruelty'

'today we are still amazed by the rendering of Proserpina's soft flesh, into which Pluto's hands are thrust'

An accompanying sculpture in the next room shows the same subject matter, this time of Daphne and Apollo.

It shows Daphne trying to escape, just as Proserpina does.

Daphne is transforming into a laurel in the process.

The accompanying text reads:

'Daphne had prayed to be dissolved or transformed, and her prayer was answered'

That is: she would rather no longer exist than be raped.

Both Daphne and Proserpina have tranquil, sleepy, almost expressionless faces that divulge barely any emotion at all.

***

Just before leaving to head to the airport, Michelle takes me up to the roof of the institute. It has the second-highest viewpoint in the whole of Rome.

'If I lived here and had this view whenever I wanted,' I say, looking out across the sepia buildings and infinite cloudy sky, 'I would feel so motivated to write.'

'If I didn't know that we would still be in contact over the next few weeks, I would find it very strange now you're going,' she says at the train station.

A few hours later, waiting for my delayed flight's departure time to be updated, I would already be missing my temporary routine that had asked so much of the best and special parts of me – and at the same time had left undisturbed or at least soothed the parts that seem to cause me the most trouble and distress.

I've surprised myself, again.

Flight time: 4.30

Expected: 6.15

LOVE

Isha Karki

[Content Note: Blood, sex, violence]

She thinks about sex.

At the library, writing a thesis on desire and violence; at the self-checkout, basket crammed with soup and unripened fruit; at night, tucking hot-water bottles snug into her body. She thinks of her open mouth, slick with spit, slipping down the length of him; his thighs trembling as she strokes his swollen head with her tongue.

At her parents' house, a mug warming her hands, watching snow masking their garden, low in her stomach, something uncoils. She feels her mother's eyes on her. She turns away to look at the untouched whiteness outside. The tea, fragrant with cinnamon and cloves, blisters when she sips it to hide her smile. In her mind, he's gripping her hips, groaning, as she slides onto him, and his hands, tight—so tight—surely, the whorls of his fingertips are imprinted onto her bones.

Her cunt throbs with the thought of it.

***

They meet after a month of selfies and small talk on Fluck, the latest dating app.

The first time, at a swimming pool: steaming water, bare skin, and the sting of chlorine. She feels his eyes track her as she emerges from the changing rooms and lets her limbs loosen. She dips her ankles into the pool; goosebumps scatter across her thighs before she steps in neck deep and submerges herself underwater. The world is hushed and dreamy. He dives in after her and they race in the fast lane, stopping only when their lungs are burning. Breathless, dripping water, they press their chests, stare at each other's water-slicked bodies, and laugh.

When the final pub calls last orders, she tries to invite him back to hers: I'd love to, he says, before the question tumbles out of her mouth.

His arm brushes hers on the sofa, but he doesn't reach for her. She can think of nothing but the heat of him, his soapy smell, and how his cock will feel, swelling inside her mouth.

Touch me, she thinks.

He goes to the toilet. Now, she thinks. Her mouth is dry; she drains her wine glass.

Can she do it?

When he returns, she walks up to him till there's a sliver of space between her nipples and him. He steps back and back till his legs meet the sofa and he sits and she climbs onto him, runs her hands down his neck, licks the wine off his lips, and puts her pussy where it's hard and hot.

Yes, she can.

* * *

I love girls who love sex, he says.

She doesn't tell him that sex has been foreign to her, that she hasn't fucked anyone in five years. She doesn't tell him this is a test: a home-coming. She smiles, lets him think what he wants, lets him say what he wants, closes her eyes and rubs her slicked lips against him over and over again.

I'd wife a slut, he says, lips curved, palm grinding against her, I know that makes me different to most guys, but I love girls who love sex.

***

They meet three times, four times a week. They end at hers, gulping wine by the bottle, ripping condom packets with teeth, pulling at each other so hard the slap of flesh rings in her ears hours later.

His mouth, hot against her cunt, feels pleasant enough. His fingers haven't quite learned how to find her clit, to part her and slide in, to cup her and make her tremble. Is this desire? She can count the number of times he has made her come – once – yet the thought of his mouth hot against her makes her wet; more so, she thinks, than when he is there, with his head between her legs, nudging her with his tongue.

***

Every day for three months, she wakes to a message from him—until one day, nothing. And the next day, nothing. And the next, nothing.

Though it's the sex that's gone—the sex, the sex, the sex—

her skin erupts. Bumpy redness on the inside of her thighs, lumped on the underside of her wrists.

She goes on Fluck, swipes, stares at the faces of strangers, puts her phone away.

She examines her fingers, at once inflamed and lacking solidity.

Desire is to be desired, she thinks. To be desired is to be brought into sharp existence.

Without his good morning gorgeous and sweet dreams babes, her days and nights lose form; she goes back to cheese, beans and toast now she can't Snap him her dinner; when she fucks herself, trying to come this thing out, she palpates shame.

Head buried under her duvet, she finally surrenders and whispers his name over and over, calling him into being: an apparition, reflected in a mirror in the dead of night.

It works.

A message appears on her phone: Hey beautiful, how's it going?

Three weeks: he doesn't say why; she can't make herself ask.

***

Months pass; he asks her to a friend's dinner party. Wear that black dress babe, he says, and them heels too, I want my girl to be the sexiest.

The dress is tight on her ribcage, but she zips it up and takes shallow breaths. She pulls on the heels though they chafe. He grabs her when she comes down the stairs, nestles his face in the curve of her neck, and she thinks the pain's worth it.

She's only ever known her parents' parties: every aunty and uncle they met since moving to the UK sitting cross-legged on the floor, knees overlapping, cushions padding tailbones, using coffee tables as perches, talking over one another. A no-shoes policy and food brought out in vats, filled with pulau and musoori dal, mountains of aloo ko achaar, bowlfuls of sadheko bhatmas, heaps of grilled chicken and mutton chops, and slivers of fatty pork, swimming in gravy.

Here, everyone's in suits and cocktail dresses, stilettos sinking into thick white carpet, as they jut their hips and lean into one another's ears. She takes a flute of champagne, wanders over to inspect a pyramid of oysters set on crushed ice.

You've never had them, right babe, he says, appearing at her side. Lemme get you some. You gotta tip the shell so the oyster slides into the back of your throat.

She's reminded of murmured bedtime lessons from her sister: take them in, right to the back of your throat, and when they come, you won't even notice.

As he returns, she thinks of them fucking right there, next to the pyramid, legs hooked around him, heels digging into his flesh, hands gripping the table as he thrusts into her, pyramid teetering, splashing them with vinegary juices.

She does as he instructs, tipping the shell, smudging lipstick on its edges; the flesh barely touches her, just a chilled thing sliding down her throat.

This is wrong, she thinks, wiping the corner of her mouth. The next one, she slides into her mouth and lets sit. It is silky and cool and salty and soft. Her nipples harden; she brushes against his arm. The corner of his mouth curves but he turns to his friends.

125

It's only when the host makes a toast—he's getting married—that she notices the shell-shaped ring box topping the pyramid. Instead of the glint of a ring though, there's something which looks like oyster flesh but is—

The champagne almost slips from her hands. She holds tight and stares.

She sees it throb—once, twice, thrice.

She thinks of the miniature slugs which appear in spring, clinging to the porcelain lip of her bathtub, slivers of black on white. That's what it looks like: tiny slugs, curled up, pulsating.

The to-be-engaged woman is dazzling. Ruby red dress, teeth gleaming, lips a gloss of blood. Her smile doesn't waver, not once in the five hours they are there, fixed as it is to her face.

She averts her eyes from the woman's teeth, feeling queasy, thinking: those fucking oysters.

**

Does he go down on you, her friends ask. She doesn't tell them her fingers do the work but how her thighs shudder, muscles clenching, drenching his mouth.

She doesn't quite know how to be in a relationship, having never been in one, she confides to them.

Bullshit, her most headstrong friend says. You're nurturing loads of relationships right now. People just shit on platonic relationships when, really, those are the ones that nourish us. I've been shaped by them, more than any half-arsed romance I've had. Look, she says, as she rolls up her sleeves.

Her arms have glittering layers of skin and bone, ossified into iron strength.

Another friend, voice quiet but steely, says: Absolutely, we get sold this fucked up idea that only romantic love will complete us. Did I tell you Parvs at work can't feel anything down there now? She gave her ex her you-know-what, thinking they were it and now... She trails off and shrugs. Her fingers, too, have the bulk of coal grinding into diamonds. She has sworn off dating, instead focusing on her art and mending her frayed relationship with her mother.

Her friends are cool and confident. She surveys their bodies, how they enunciate, sit straight, wear what they want, eat what they want, meet who they want, fuck only when they want.

It's not for everyone.

She thinks of her life with her parents: buried like the garden under snow. Then, she thinks of the lustre of her fingernails as she takes his leaking dick into her mouth, of her toes curling into bed sheets as he angles his hips and thrusts. When he's inside her, she feels—unfurled—her brown body, for once, emerging, breathing.

But the sex, someone says with a laugh. She's talking about a relationship with sex.

Yeah, whatever you say, I'd be nothing without Jase, a small voice, Riya's, pipes up from the corner.

They all grow quiet; someone suggests paying the bill. No-one says they can barely see the outline of Riya's body: eyes, nose, mouth, now just pencil smudges on her face; she is disappearing.

***

That night, when he's lying on top of her, body flush against her back, the weight of him almost too much to bear, she remembers the oysters, wonders how it would feel to carve out that precious piece of yourself and hand it over like so. She could never do it—succumb to a life without pleasure — yet, she feels another part of her body responding, the flesh below her ribcage loosening.

***

She persuades him to go on a hike: a simulated experience, the jungles of South East Asia in Northumberland, the website says. Five minutes in, his clothes are soaked. Half an hour, they stop, his skin blooming red; he swats at the mosquitoes buzzing around their sticky bodies. The cicadas screech, so loud, she tells him he could kill her and no-one would hear her scream. He stares for a moment, then laughs, and the sound of it is swallowed up.

He gives up after an hour and they fuck against a tree, bark cutting her skin. Panting, she tells him she's scratched up and bleeding and he digs in his fingers, hard, and comes immediately. She finishes the hike alone, semen seeping down her thighs, sweat stinging her cuts.

***

Months into their fucking, she comes with his dick inside her. It's the first time—and she cradles his head as they lie entwined in aftershocks, overcome with something.

She decides then to give it to him. She'll never be able to surrender what others before her have, but she can give him this much.

She caresses the flesh, just under her ribs, on the right curve of her body, where it's coming loose, has been coming loose for months, though she pretended not to notice. She tears in with her nails, scoops out a chunk of herself, and holds in her hands the pulpy mess of it.

He puts his palms over hers—clumps of blood-soaked flesh lay clasped between them, trying to escape from the gaps in her fingers—he leans in, and says, Let's stick it in the freezer, babe.

He doesn't ask if it hurts.

The next day, she handwashes the sheets, scrubs the spots — but the stains won't go.

***

Jesus, look at this girl's photo, he says, pointing at some-one's Instagram. Her boobs and all these thirsty creeps. Sure, they're gorgeous tits, but when girls put themselves out there—

He looks up and perhaps sees something in her face. He breaks into a smile and whispers: Nothing will do for me but your little plums though, babe.

He slips her t-shirt off and touches her breasts. Her limbs are stiff; she feels cold although the heating blasts.

It's her body, she thinks.

***

Babe, can't we? he asks, and it's the first time he asks but not the last time. I just wanna taste it.

She's been slicing courgettes with precise speed; now, her

Isha Karki

hands still. Her hold on the knife is so tight, it trembles.

Can't we try a bit? I just wanna, he whispers between her ear lobe and neck, Lick it. His tongue darts out and the sensation shoots to her groin. Just like I lick you, just like I love tasting the rest of you. He slips his fingers into her underwear, parts her folds and nudges them inside. Takes them out to suck on them, hums.

Her thighs are shaking.

Desire, she thinks. Must be.

Jason and Riya swear by it, he says, I've never seen him so happy.

Only when he goes to the fridge, takes a beer and wanders out the kitchen does she try to straighten her fingers. But she finds she can't let go of the knife.

***

At night, she dreams it talking to her: the hole in her body, a voice from deep underwater.

Feed me, it says.

But it hushes and won't speak when she asks it how.

***

For two weeks, she walks around with a bad smell under her nose. She thinks it's leaking gas, but the suppliers come to check and say nothing's wrong, and she thinks it's the pipes, sewage ripening in the freak heatwave, but the plumbers say nothing's wrong. She throws out all the fruit and veg. She cleans out the fridge and scours the oven, pouring bleach down sink holes.

130

Only when she steps out of her clothes and scrubs herself raw with a pumice stone does she understand where the stench comes from.

She makes an appointment with the GP.

There's nothing wrong, the doctor says when it's finally her turn.

She points to her gaping side. The stench. The congealed pus. The doctor steeples his fingers with seriousness but doesn't look at the scooped-out flesh once. He mentions therapy, but the smell is so overpowering, she feels faint and cannot listen.

She goes to a sexual health clinic and waits and waits. The receptionist keeps glancing at her, still typing up the reason of her visit. When she's seen, the doctor listens to her for a few seconds, before holding up a hand, and lifting her own shirt to reveal a cratered body, deep holes littering her flesh.

I couldn't bear to give them too much at once, the doctor says, laughing and not laughing at the same time, And now I'm like the moon.

No, nothing can be done to eradicate the smell completely.

I'm prescribing you antibiotics for the infection – most women swear by this one – the opening should close up, and the rancidness should lessen to a whiff.

***

That night, gripped in an antibiotics-induced fever, a half-memory, slurred and hazy, breaks free.

A drunken night—her face crushed into the pillow—limbs molten and floppy—a splitting pressure in her ass—she doesn't move—can't move—

Isha Karki

In the morning, he'd said, I was a bit rough yesterday, huh, but you took it like a champ, and kissed her on the head.

Her body seeps with the memory and later, when he grips her waist and fucks her hard, she wants to be gripped tight, so tight, that her bones crack.

***

Babe, he says as soon as she walks through the front door, I cooked dinner. You're gonna love it—I made the sauce extra spicy—and there's something special in today's dish, just wait and see.

When she enters the kitchen and sees his teeth gleaming, she knows.

Her bones lock in place. Pus trickles down the length of her.

What? He says. Why you looking at me like that?

He comes to her and puts his hands on her shoulders the smell of charred flesh clings to his clothes – he steers her to the dining table where a plate is set for her, cutlery and napkin on the side, red wine in a glass, and nudges her into the chair.

She sits.

Go on, babe, try it, he says.

He picks up the spoon and scoops up some of the meat, presenting it with a flourish.

She looks at him, sweat beading his forehead, skin creased up in joy, his eyes wide with excitement.

She finds her own face fixed into a dazzling smile.

She takes the spoon—and opens her mouth.

HOW TO WIN AT THE GAME OF LIFE

Kate Young

[Content Note: sexual assault in non-specific detail.]

> '...when you realise you want to spend the rest of your life
> with somebody, you want the rest of your life to start as
> soon as possible.'
>
> Harry Burns, *When Harry Met Sally*

On Saturdays at our dad's house, when we were small, my sister and I would play endless rounds of The Game of Life. Did your family have it too? Perhaps not; if you're not familiar with it, it's a bright, cheesy, colourful board game, where you place yourself (a pink or blue peg) into a tiny plastic car and spin the wheel. The board takes you through all of life's major milestones – you might find a cure for cancer, or go on a cruise, or become an Olympian, or paint a masterpiece. But before you embark on any of this, the game stops you in your tracks. About ten spaces in you've graduated university or entered the workforce, and now it's time to get married.

In The Game of Life, your wedding isn't a space you can breeze past – there's an octagonal stop sign and an image of a cheerfully grinning (heterosexual, white) couple looking up at you. As a ten-year-old I never questioned it. I dutifully added a blue peg beside the pink one already slotted into my car, and spun the wheel again, collecting a house, and then some children on subsequent turns. The game confirmed everything I was anticipating about adulthood: that life in the future held the promise of a husband, a collection of kids, and a cottage in the countryside somewhere, with a row of dirty Wellington boots by the door.[3] Despite allergies that made my eyes itch and throat swell up, there was even a loveable family hound in the picture too – ideally the one Hallie (American Lindsay Lohan) had in *The Parent Trap*.

My teenage years did little to dissuade me of these notions of family and of romance. I fell in love with nineteenth-century romance novels, and late twentieth-century romantic comedies, long before I started falling in love with any boys. I yearned for a relationship like the one in *When Harry Met Sally*: a quick-witted, laid-back Harry Burns to complement my uptight, perfectionist Sally Albright, or for someone like *You've Got Mail*'s Joe Fox, who would send me a bouquet of sharpened pencils when the autumn leaves started to fall (they didn't really fall in

---

3 It is perhaps important to note here that this was far from the only part of my future that I had planned out in detail. I had grand (and specific) plans for my career too – at various points I imagined myself as an author, a criminal barrister, the first female Prime Minister of Australia, and (for my later years at school) a paediatric surgeon. I finally settled on training as a drama and biology teacher. I committed to each of these imagined futures with a compulsive vigour, but the photograph on my future work desk never changed: husband, kids, cottage, Wellington boots.

Brisbane, but that was beside the point). I dreamed of meeting a man like Austen's Frederick Wentworth who would write me achingly romantic letters, making declarations that went something along the lines of: '*You pierce my soul... I have loved none but you. Unjust I may have been, weak and resentful I have been, but never inconstant. You alone have brought me to Bath.*' I was young and impressionable, and nowhere had ever sounded more romantic than Bath.

I didn't date much in secondary school; my focus invariably fell on calculus, countless school clubs and choirs, and saving enough from my part-time job to fund the long-planned move to England. I met some good lads and snogged a bunch of them on dance floors, but there was no-one I fancied enough to draw me away from writing assignments on stem cell research or from *Much Ado About Nothing*. I fell hard for a guy in my first year of university – a relationship that began as a summer romance and reinforced every romantic ideal I had harboured to this point. In the end, a long-distance relationship just didn't work for us. As the end of university approached, and my plans for England began to come to fruition, I felt secretly relieved that I could happily wave farewell to Brisbane, without any romantic entanglements to unknit.

My first year in England was overwhelming. I had left my quiet, comfortable, suburban childhood for the grey skies and greyer streets of Whitechapel. I worked all hours, hopeful of 'making it' in theatre, and formed tentative, promising friendships, with people as unfamiliar with the city as I was. Dating was tricky – Tinder was years away from being a fixture on our phones, and working in teaching and in theatre didn't introduce me to many eligible men. But I wasn't too worried. I had all the time in the world.

My life changed when I was twenty-two. Less than a year after the big move, I was sexually assaulted. Unable to process what had happened, and with a support network that still felt relatively new, I buried those hours deep within myself and managed to keep them hidden for the next couple of years. But it ate away at me, consuming my hopeful, cheerful dreams for the future, and forcing me to retreat into myself. Eventually, I came to accept that keeping the secret was an impossibility, and the truth came out in a rush to a friend one night. Once I had shone a light on it, this darkest and most shameful part of my narrative, there was no way of burying it again.

The next few years were complicated. Though externally I managed to make it appear as if I was coping, the reality was very different. I felt like my insides alternated between being made of sherbet that fizzed and frothed uncontrollably and made me jittery with nerves, or with cement, which sent me into a torpor. I couldn't ride the Tube at rush hour, sit in a crowded theatre, or go on a date without risking a full-blown panic attack. My hair fell out in clumps, I suffered from debilitating insomnia, and my anxiety levels were at breaking point.

Most tangibly, I felt an overwhelming sense of shame and struggled with a toxic hatred of the body (my body) that had failed me so completely. I had always assumed I would be able to fight my way out of any situation I needed to escape. The reality was very different: when push came to shove, I froze instead. A round of cognitive behavioural therapy on the NHS helped with the day-to-day; after six months on the waiting list and sixteen Thursday morning sessions I could sit in the middle of a row in the theatre again, and my commute to and from work slowly became easier. But the self-hatred ran deep.

I began to feel unworthy of my friendships, of those rich relationships I had so lovingly cultivated. Though my dear friends rallied around me, I struggled with how needy I was – I both craved constant companionship, and second-guessed and judged every moment I spent in the company of my friends. I was certain I was boring everyone, pushing them all away when I needed them most. Scared of losing them for good, I stopped making plans and retreated, finally reaching a point where I was spending much of my time alone. It goes without saying that meeting someone in a romantic context felt out of the question. And so, to my despair, my long-standing life plan – the husband, the children and the house – stalled.

In this state, I returned, for comfort, to my old favourites. I watched romantic comedies on a loop, revelling in their deeply reassuring narratives, so constant and predictable. I relaxed into *North and South* and *Sense and Sensibility*, where the barriers to love were ones I knew would be resolved by the final chapter. My hopeless romantic teenage self began to resurface, and I came to the conclusion that my 'recovery' was inextricably linked with finding a man who felt safe, and who I wanted to date. Meet cute after meet cute danced across the screen or page in front of me, and I imagined how a flirtation might start: in an UberPool after leaving a friend's dinner party? In the bar after work after he got my whiskey with one ice cube and I got his with a splash of water? As we both reached for the same crate of tomatoes at the farmers' market? But it was nothing more than intangible imagining; the idea of putting myself back out there for real was terrifying.

After a couple of years of waiting to feel ready, I made a decision. Despite my inclination to hibernate, and to hide myself away from the world, I forced myself to date. I resolved to fake it until I could make it, and went for dinner with a few lovely men, dating just enough that I could convince myself that I was trying. I had managed to trap myself in a strange catch-22: I had decided that getting better meant falling into bed (and a relationship) with someone, but this wasn't something I could do without dating, whether I felt ready for it or not.

While I continued to wrestle with dating and recovery, the rest of my life progressed regardless. I started a new creative project, that gradually became a career. I began to feel tentatively more in control of my life again. But it looked nothing like I had anticipated. I was approaching thirty, and had been single since university; miles away from the family I was still sure I wanted. I came to a revolutionary (read: uncomfortably, glaringly obvious) conclusion. Perhaps before I could repair my relationship with men, I needed to repair my relationship with myself.

* * *

The trouble was, I had no idea how to begin. How does one cultivate a relationship with oneself? I had no road map for this; none of my old dependable books or films could help me navigate it. And it wasn't something I knew how to speak about. I knew how to be a loving daughter, a kind and dependable friend, a devoted sister. I knew what I hoped falling in love, and fostering a romantic relationship, might look like. But I had no idea where to start when the relationship in question was the problematic one I had with myself. The disconnect I felt with my body, and the ongoing struggle with feelings of anxiety and worthlessness, weren't something I could brush over or solve quickly. These feelings felt insurmountable, and I started to fear that I might have to accept their persistent presence in my life as inevitable costs of that night when I was twenty-two, and my response in the years since.

Without any specific purpose in mind, I joined the local lido and started to swim. I challenged the body I so deeply mistrusted (and that I blamed for the situation I now found myself in) to make its way down lap after quiet lap. With my head below the water, I realised how reliant I had become on chatter: on an episode of *Parks and Recreation* playing in the background, on the comforting hum of the radio, on a podcast about murder or etymology or *The West Wing*. I was dependent upon something to distract me from the constant negativity in my own head. In London Fields Lido, all I could hear was my breath and the rush of water past my ears. I had been drowning that voice out for years, terrified of what I would find.

In the pool, it accompanied me up and down the lane; there was no avoiding it. I took breaks at the end of the lane, not to catch my breath, but to give myself a moment of comforting chatter from the changing rooms, or the kids splashing in the lane next to me. Instead of drowning out the negativity and fear with incessant noise, once in the water I had to tune in to what I was thinking, to hopes and fears and thoughts both significant and insignificant. Nothing changed overnight, but I slowly started to connect with myself again. I began to question what it was I wanted, rather than defaulting to a path of least conflict, and least resistance, in a desperate bid to please those around me and keep them on side. I started to make plans for the future and considered for the first time what life might look like if it didn't have to include the husband, kids, cottage and Wellington boots. It was difficult, and emotionally draining, but I could feel something start to shift.

About a year after I visited the pool, I allowed myself to be dragged on a run with a triathlete friend. An unenthusiastic runner from my primary school days (I was the one at the back during cross country, gossiping with a friend or two, and breaking into a half-hearted run whenever we spotted a teacher), I expected to loathe the experience. I was validated over the next thirty minutes. I hated the feeling of it: the ache in my calves, the inefficiency of my sports bra, the irritating certainty that my 'jogging' wasn't actually any faster than my regular walking pace. But I stubbornly kept it up and started to alternate between mornings in the pool and a loop around Clapham Common. As my feet pounded the pavement, I worked to keep my breath in time. In time I started to come without my headphones, leaving comforting distractions back in the house, and those thirty minutes in the park were much like the ones I spent in the water: I was unable to avoid whatever it was that was running through my head.

It is difficult to pinpoint precisely when I started to look forward to these half-hour blocks of time spent on my own. For so long, being left alone with my thoughts had been debilitating; my head full of hateful commentary, passing minutes and hours in anxiety, convinced that my solitude was a reflection of how people felt about me. I distracted myself as best I could – I read, and cooked, went for walks and had long baths – but the hours were rarely pleasant ones. They felt out of my control, a default situation I found myself in when I didn't have plans and wasn't at work.

Eventually, this began to shift. I eagerly anticipated the alone time in the pool or the park and was reluctant to agree to social invitations that would mean I wasn't able to fit it into my day. My plans for the future developed and crystallised; I discovered that if I moved out of London, I might just be able to afford a small place of my own to buy. I decided to move forward with life on my own terms, no longer doggedly focused on finding someone to share the milestones with. I became impatient for this new chapter of my life to start – I had been waiting for so long to meet someone who would trigger that 'next phase', that 'rest of your life' that Harry Burns shouts about to Sally Albright. In the end, I still can't quite believe how simple it was. I had always been the one with power over that trigger.

I have thought a lot in the past couple of years about the distinction between being 'lonely', being 'alone' and being 'on my own'. I have come to appreciate that I am now often on my own, and am sometimes lonely, but I rarely feel entirely alone. I have so many extraordinary and richly rewarding relationships – friends I can call or visit, a family who span continents (and who are thankfully always on WhatsApp). My moments of feeling lonely mostly feel natural, as if they're merely a reminder to pick up my phone and make a plan with a friend.

Nowadays, I am particularly fastidious in planning the time I spend on my own; I commit to it like I would time spent with a dear friend. I make sure I am on time, trying not to allow work to spill over into my evening (the line is all too easy to blur when my work desk is in my bedroom at home). I make a plan for something I know I will enjoy; I might head out for lunch with a book, or take a long walk along the canal, or catch a film at the cinema. Of course, I still have bad days. I am an anxious person by nature and tend to catastrophise situations. But I am kinder to myself generally, taking time to process and challenge the negative narrative when it inevitably surfaces, and that kindness has been the most measurable difference in my relationship with myself. And for the first time in years, I feel comfortable, even proud, about what I bring to the table. I am happy being on my own. Meeting someone I want to spend more time with now feels like a bonus, not a requirement.

A couple of years ago, I played The Game of Life as a nanny, with my two charges. After starting the game with one pink peg in my plastic car, I added another pink peg when I was stopped at the marriage line. My charges never questioned it, but to me it felt thrillingly transgressive: a small breaking of those rules I had so dutifully followed as a child. The next time we played I confidently breezed past the stop sign, telling the kids that I didn't fancy getting married this time. The game continued regardless, of course. I could still buy a house and have children, and find a cure for cancer. It felt right, and reflected the real life I had built: I was happy, truly happy, sitting in the car on my own.

MADE VISIBLE BY DISTANCE

Anna Kahn

I took one of my favourite photos of my flatmate in the park on a snatched weekday we both had free. She was photographing trees, pointedly, because I'd insisted it was too hot to brave the bus to Epping Forest to visit proper trees. I had my phone out for selfies, my lipstick and sunglasses and a floppy hat I'd nicked off her. I looked up and she was standing, as she often does, with all her weight into one hip, looking so much like herself.

I got six shots, two of them good: one of her looking down at the camera and one of her raising it to the foliage, blurred so that it was unidentifiable in her hands. I cropped the trees to look like a full woodland. She could have been praying, or dancing. Something more forest than human. She made the second one her profile picture.

I haven't taken many photos of her. We spend so much time two sofa cushions apart, more evenings together than not, but so far it only occurs to me to make a record when she's far away.

***

I hadn't wanted to move out of my last (raucous, international) house share, but the landlord decided to sell up and return to Jamaica. I chose to move in with my flatmate for two reasons: she had the most opulently gorgeous cats I've ever met, and she said in her advert that she didn't care about ethnicity or gender or sexuality.

It's a depressing challenge, looking for rooms in London as a queer with a last name which makes you sound less white than you look, when you actually are less white than you look, but in a different way than your name makes it sound. When the email asks where are you from, you have to guess whether the writer wants to hear a little village in Buckinghamshire or half Iraqi, quarter German, quarter Latvian, because if you get it wrong you don't hear back, and almost nobody wants to hear both.

I went round to view the flat. Our smiles startled each other at first: we have the same teeth, a big gap between the front two. Eyecatch grins. Her hair was darker than it had looked on her Gmail avatar, so it was like looking at a fairer-skinned version of myself. A somewhat dazing experience.

She was much quieter than the other potential flatmates I was talking to, the occupants of a house in Brixton where everyone smoked indoors and danced in the kitchen on the regular. Another me in another universe is probably very happy (and quite drunk) there, but my flatmate made an offer first, so here I am, sober.

Apart from halls at uni, my flatmate is only the second person I've lived with who grew up with two English parents. She's the only person I've lived with one-on-one. A two-bed flat with one quiet person differs from a three-and-a-half-floor house with six shouty ones. That's before you even factor in Englishness, the way English people won't tell you when they're upset, the way you just have to know them well enough to divine it from their silences.

In three years my flatmate and I have not had a single blazing row, but I don't know if that's because I've never made her blazingly angry or because she would never initiate a row even if she were blazingly angry enough for one.

Salaam, the most opulently furred of her cats, was hit by a car while my flatmate was in the Lake District. Our next-door neighbour found him, banged on our door, cradled him and carried him in on a waft of aftershave and weed. It was the hottest part of the summer. I hadn't really got up yet – yesterday's dress pulled on to answer the door, no bra, no deodorant – and the fear sweat off both of us was awful. We knew Salaam was dead, but we went through the motions – I called a taxi to the vet, the neighbour lent me cash for it, we got Salaam into the carry basket. We waited. The neighbour carried him to the taxi for me.

I rang my flatmate, rang and rang and rang her in the taxi. No answer. The vet asked if my flatmate would want Salaam cremated. I had no idea. He gave me some leaflets for my flatmate to read, said they'd keep the body until a decision was made but that I should nudge my flatmate towards cremation if I could because after a few days in the freezer it's not very nice.

I wandered out, dehydrated and not tracking all that well, wishing I was wearing a bra. I found a park. I sat on the swings and called my flatmate again. No answer. I left a message. I'm so sorry. I'm so sorry.

She got it two hours later when she'd climbed high enough for signal. She called me straight back. We'd been living together for eight or nine months but this was the first time I'd heard her voice on the phone. It was wrong, and not just because of the tears. Too high, too much treble, all the bass filtered out of her.

She cut her holiday short. I can't remember if I gave her a hug when she got back, which makes me think I didn't, because I think I can remember all the times I've hugged her, the weird, sudden presence of her body as a physical experience rather than an object to be observed.

Her copy of *Lemonade* had arrived while she'd been away; she is someone who buys physical copies of all the music she likes. We decided to watch it, because we didn't know what else to do. I poured us some squash while she put it on, only she couldn't get it to play. I said, have you put the CD in instead of the DVD? and she looked and said, no, no I have not, in a way that absolutely meant yes, yes I have, and it was not that funny but we broke down laughing, that heaving gulping laugh which passes between two people who are close to tears and which feels like an alternative to the threatened crying but which is actually just the crying with hiccups.

My flatmate likes shows about murder. She's watched every single Netflix-available episode of *Forensic Files* twice: once by herself, once with me. When I first moved in I'd eat in my room, legacy habit from ceding the old living room to my old housemate who had a ten-year-old and so needed the space. Once my flatmate relaxed enough to start watching *Forensic Files* in front of me I got hooked. When we're both in we eat dinner together and watch whatever murder-related stuff we can find on Netflix, while the cats wander between us for maximal scritch reception.

We fret sometimes that we're turning into a single person. We didn't start with much distance: our first names are very similar and our full names have the same scansion. There is the gap in our teeth. We are too serious and too sarcastic at the same time. We don't like people.

I listen to the *Mountain Goats* now. She winds the imaginary handle on her phone when it is taking a while to load. Our speech patterns are blending; we both come from dialect-heavy families, used to adding new extravagances to a shared vocabulary. Sometimes there are clashes: her family's *vegegaburbles* have won over my family's *veJETables*, but the fight was long and vicious. Sometimes my dad will say something my flatmate's family say, which he has picked up through me because he's never met her, and I will realise how out of control the whole situation has become.

My flatmate's one pair of formal-enough-for-occasional-fancy-consulting boots fell apart just as she had to do some fancy consulting. I said, do you want to borrow my black boots? and she said, I don't think they'll fit and I don't think they're formal enough, and I said, no worries. A few days later she came home with a new pair of formal-enough-for-occasional-fancy-consulting boots, and they were the same model as mine in the same size. They looked formal enough in the shop, apparently. We've had to lace them differently so we can tell them apart.

***

Our lives outside our immediate neighbourhood have very little overlap, but we do London stuff sometimes. Fancy ice cream. The Natural History Museum. A gig in Vauxhall, in a pub on a boat with a fixed mooring.

Anna Kahn

My flatmate was late for the gig because she reached the point where it looked like CityMapper was actively bullshitting about knowing where the boat was and she lost her nerve and retraced her steps, instead of forging on towards the lights which looked like they might form the shape of a boat if you came closer.

I hovered on the gangway waiting for her. I saw a body walking towards me along the riverfront and even though I could see very little by the streetlights I knew it was her from the bobbing of the white star on her jumper, the familiar wave, more up and down than is typical, and the light just catching the outlines of her arms, held tight at the elbow and loose at the wrist. Like a penguin, she said when I tried to mime her gait for her during the interval. Yes, like a penguin.

She wasn't wearing it that day, but I am a big fan of my flatmate's coat. It flares sharply at the waist: a little bit princess, a little bit goth Riding Hood. I can see just a corner of its fake-fur trim from the other end of the supermarket now and know it for hers, feel a private spike of satisfaction that she is heading to the checkout and we will be going home soon.

This is not to say I always recognise her when she's wearing it. One time I watched her come through our literal front gate and thought she was a stranger, because she was wearing a hat. When I said I hadn't recognised her, she said, yes, I was wearing a hat, like that is a legitimate reason not to recognise the person you've spent the majority of your evenings looking at for the last three years.

***

My flatmate had to have a nerve injection at the beginning of last summer. The information sheet said she needed a responsible adult to make sure she got home safely. I went with her, both of us cracking jokes about whether or not I constituted a responsible adult.

She was told not to eat in the morning. We turned up at the appointed time and were split up, me to the waiting room and her to a curtained-off bed, clothes off, gown on, at which point they mentioned that she might not be seen for some time, and they were out of vegetarian sandwiches and so would only have biscuits to feed her afterwards.

She sent me a picture of her socks. She sent me a text about how hungry she was. She sent me a text about the sandwich situation. She sent me a lot of sobbing emojis. I was having quite a nice time in the waiting room, co-editing an essay with my parents, and I felt very guilty. She was only twenty feet or so away, but the waiting room door and the curtain around her bed might as well have had locks on them.

I left the hospital and walked back towards the train station until I found a supermarket. I bought two quiches and some crisps. I ate mine in the park outside the hospital, enjoying the novelty of sun on my shoulders.

Back into the waiting room. Another hour passed, then two. My flatmate texted that she was going in. Not long now. I wrapped up the conversation I was having with a poet-friend in New York and packed up my shit. My flatmate texted that it was done, that she had to sit for a few minutes and then she was allowed to put clothes on.

The nurse came into the waiting room already speaking, caught eyes with me mid-sentence and froze: I'm looking for [flatmate's]... [beat of silence]... friend. That hesitation. You could see the word LESBIANS flashing across the insides of her eyes, even though my flatmate had written 'flatmate' on her paperwork. I can't remember what I was wearing but I must have looked somehow queerer than the nurse had expected.

My flatmate demolished her quiche. I got her home safely enough.

***

We had a hell of a summer altogether. Briefly: aforementioned nerve injection, broken limb (her), paranoia and illusions, worsening tremor (me), the NHS taking a long time to handle referrals (both of us), at interlocking times a roof leak, a bathroom leak, no boiler, no hob, no oven, no kitchen ceiling, the entire flat full of horrible acrylic dust, an injured cat who needed twice-daily eye drops which he hated, and the nights so hot that none of us slept properly for three weeks straight, cats included. It got so that every new thing which went wrong felt inevitable. The heaving, gulping laugh made a lot of appearances. Nobody else could understand the gravity or the ridiculousness of the situation.

By the end of the hell of the summer we were running on fumes. My flatmate was sad that she hadn't made it to the seaside. She specified that she wanted a sandy beach, no pebbles, so we went to Shoeburyness because someone had told me it was nice. It was not as nice as I had been led to believe, but it was broadly fine.

We got chips from a van. Cans of coke. It was cloudy, for once; we needed the light jackets we'd brought. The wind was up enough that the family forty feet over kept trying to fly a kite, but not enough for it to actually lift.

We set up camp on raised ground next to the firing range. Beach towels and everything. My flatmate picked her way to the waterline, to say hello to the sea, she said. She stood with all her weight into one hip, looking so much like herself.

You can't not love someone, after you go through a summer like that with them. I thought of the photos I had taken in the park. My dad, who is an accomplished photographer, says that you can tell when the person behind the camera loves the person they are photographing. I wanted to know how the photos would look now.

I took out my phone. My tremor was bad enough that only a couple of shots came out in focus. She looked like herself, surrounded by grey. I don't know what I was expecting.

When I showed her, she said, I look like I just came out of the sea, I look like I'm about to do a murder, and she was right, and she was pleased, and I was so glad I had thought to take them.

OVER

So Mayer

Medusa is over. You know that. Over: Tiresias (as in
~ the rainbow outside ~ there). Over emself
& the whole art thing. As in: over,
move on. Nothing to see here because ey're making
nothing. Because others are making, something. Ey hook up
with a linguist on Tinder look up words for
the things ey are notmaking

stele (◀ɴ) *steely*) funerary   urns (& customs)
earth & stone   lusterware   megaliths
barrows those   corbelled beehive tombs in Mycenae
ey cried in   things, ey think, to *put over*
to mark over   over & over until you remember it's
muscle memory the only way   so ey goes on the date

it is (not) like *Arrival* (Medusa the physicist now?) (well
I guess I'm not a potter anymore) (notartist) (so alien
this experience) hey let's have coffee   *So you're a linguist?*
Linguisist? Linguisticsist? Yeah she says flicking her
tongue ring it's ridiculous isn't it? My parents
called me Vāc so I was like bound to, you know? Study
Sanskrit and then I got really into it like what even

is language. What is a word a sentence a a a meaning? I mean...

Heeeeeeeeere's *coffee*. Or, per Vāc:

> It turns out that particular spatial relations have non-trivial consequences that are meaningful to humans. The spatial scene involving *on* also involves a support function between the table and the cup; unless enough of the cup's base is situated on the table, the cup will fall and smash on the floor. Equally, the spatial scene relating to *in* involves a containment function, which encompasses several consequences such as locating and limiting the activities of the contained entity. Being contained in the cup prevents the coffee from spreading out over the table; if we move the cup, the coffee moves with it. These consequences, as well as the spatio-physical configuration between entities, give rise to a range of non-spatial meanings associated with the spatial particles *on* and *in*.[1]

Oh. M thinks. K.

No. Coffee I made (once and again) (for T) *in* the cups
I made (once and over again) on the table I made
(yes just once that one) (with Chrys, skiphunter) in my studio
gone into   dust or, disuse (by me, ey think scrupulously)
(*someone else's hands on my wheel* goes through eir body
ghost over my grave is it   or *goose*?)
Ey asks the prof who shrugs and says she's not a prof not
yet but maybe if she can finish her book

---

1   Andrea Tyler and Vyvyan Evans, *The Semantics of English Prepositions: Spatial Scenes, Embodied Meaning and Cognition*, xi.

but the teaching load & she can't find a title oh and also
she doesn't rly do proverbs – or titles, ha, or like being
good with words really, with big words. *Oh.* Yeah, I do
small words   prepositions pronouns particles   parts
I like   like ligaments   they get no love
but hold it all together   like   you have beautiful hands
you know, oh, excuse me (*beautiful* thinks Medusa
callous   all the burns & cuts   split knuckles
gone nails   small parts crushed in the pursuit of
what   thick with dark hair and scars   coffee *in*
eir hands) *Tell me* — I mean, sorry, I mean – *about pre
positions pronouns particles*   Heh she says I guess you know
more about pronouns than me [*laughs*] & Medusa is back
on the doctor's table age seven   age nine   eleven
twenty (*on* implies responsibility; consequentiality)
ey get up to go realise the café's cashless   so that means
the till no   throwing change on the table   on &
Vāc says Sorry sorry for someone who studies language
really I mean I am crap at it using it I think that's why
it interests me so much like: how?   helplesswideeyedshrug
& it is not that M is unintrigued *Yeah like how I ask
myself that   a lot I'm not sure if clay was my question
or my answer to er to how how to be on this earth* of
this earth Ha says Vāc. Exactly. She pays for their
coffees with her phone & they start walking up
Grove Road towards Bethnal Green (I work near here
yeah back that way   did you know it's the only campus
with a graveyard? they found during construction it's
Sephardi although well the language is called Ladino
here's a pic of the graves) matrix
of grey weathered stones fenced

off – *Off what?* Right haha, the answers to like: how?
Answer? (longing for). No I think answers. Lots
of them which is good for how we do, I dunno, this?
Walking talking together thing (M flashes on T
one time   and again   every time walking with their cane
saying "and Judith Butler says, wait I'm para
phrasing, no-one walks without a technique of walking;
without support for that technique,[2] meaning — "a pause
for breath & a short flight of stairs taking M's arm
where [which time] outside the British Library outside
~ there) *OK* says M to cover eir absence (outside etc)
but then isn't if it answers like:how a
preposition isn't it an adverb? Like walking casually
slowly... Romantically? she quirks (*oh fuck*) Sure
that's like *how* how paint the pict- no, wait like
painting on the glaze right? That's what you
[*quirks*] But the the the mechanics the er
should I say clay of it (*with their cane: glaze or clay?*)

    we are *beside* each other

    we are *on* the oops sorry [cyclists!] pavement

    we are *in* a city or we'd probs never have met

    we are listening *to* (?) each other (?)

aware *of* the unsaid question marks the   shelllike
of Vāc's ear line of her profile *against* the shell
of the climbing wall (*all those neon plastic extrusions*
are they cups? do they hold in? on?) *And that*
like the cup it has consequences, right? If we are
in *conversation then* – It has to be strong enough
yeah to hold it like if you're uh *in* love then love

---

2   Butler in conversation with Sunaura Taylor, in the film *Examined Life*
(Astra Taylor, 2008)

has to contain you & when it moves you like the coffee
in the cup you have to go with it or   Vāc turns them
into Victoria Park   *But love* says M *that's not
a thing a substance it's not material I can't* make
love uh make things out of *love* (ey hears emself
even before Vāc's eyeroll) *you know not* out here
striking the halfgrassy late spring (and it's been *late*
this year) earth they sit down on down-   on-   M

is vertiginous with this new like a sixth sense of (of!)
direction body *in* space   hanging like those
CG monoliths that made her feel   feelings
that   tremble of *I want to   make
that happen*   that suspension of   not just body/space
old composite ey have worked with/in IN *OK how
do you work* in *love like: how?* Totally. Vāc rolls a spliff
on the cover of her iPad, which is violet, Love is
an abstract concept of course but this guy this
what did you say linguisticist ha! George Lakoff OK
he knows how how to use language to talk about itself
and stuff and he says it's in this book called *Women,
Fire and* uh *Dangerous Things* (*kiln inme inrush*
flush of is it perimenopause or memory of the night
[first and again and again] they [them-they, *les deux*
as T would say] made   that fucking clay duck   *goose*   ~
one's grave

it's the spliff smell of it *Proustian* T would say
eyeroll for the impossible to resist clichés of queer
ness because originality is one also, a Eurowestern
individualist myth we all have lineage, Medusa, they

157

would say, we all come *from*   *of*   *with*   *about*
we are between / toward / beneath / inside
oh ohhhhhhhhhhhhhhhhhhhh) *Sorry* Sorry *Sorry I was*
somewhere else uh George Layoffs? Lakoff right he says
ok first that categories and concepts do not have fixed
boundaries *Oh really* [*eyeroll*] Yeah linguistics
is a bit stating the obvious sometimes just wait he says
our conceptual systems emerge out of embodiment
and that's why say prepositions are all directions
not just for describing actually going or doing but
thinking *about* musing *on* falling *in* – So it's uh it's a
(the word emerges from ~ there) phenomenology *of prepositions*
Actually that's that's amazing Imma   She opens
the iPad and tells Siri to voice memo while M makes
a little mound of ash and dry earth   *on* not *over*

ey realise
on as in their hands on my thighs
                their tongue on my clit
                their ass on my cock
                their head on my shoulder
                their eyelashes on their cheek   fuck on
never stops & eir tears turn the mound to mud
(dissolving o_n, ey think, with that inner
wry smile that *is* T that ey read in a book Athena
gave em [this will help you deal M, it's not
self-help it's a feminist history of
psychoanalysis] [classic A] is called in- trojection
so T held an image of M and M holds an image of T
and the former is   gone
and the latter is   unchanging

and do ey need to throw that *out* or get the first back
or cups within cups   mirrors within mirrors
it is   lustreware, high gloss or perhaps under
glass as when in a gallery and the spotlight throws
off or *up*   you cannot touch)   and that's what's
important following Lakoff, Vāc continues into air,
that we cannot be do not want to be abstract
we want to do through the body even when it's what's
on ha *on* our minds say when we grieve we grieve *over*
and that's because we know the posture / setting / direction
it IS phenomenal   literally   oh shit She shuts
the cover & they watch a child in bright green dungarees
& a caliper brace fall over & their sibling drop down
dramatically at their side   get up & go over

over again   together, and Vāc says Interestingly
over is like *the* classic preposition in linguistics
debates because it's supercomplicated   like *over* what?
What did that kid trip over? And over how? It encompasses
kinds of *on*   kinds of *above* both   still and moving
touching and uh not touching   and that's just emm in
physical   *Consequential* says M gathering emself
up

(*by convention we agree to think that what we assimilate
in our minds to* above *and* before, *&c. is better than what
we designate by* below *and* behind, *&c. though there can
be neither* up *nor* down, *before* nor *after, in what is*

purely mental,[3]

M reads later during a random Google search while leaving
(...) bubbling in response to Vāc's Let's meet up (ha! why up?
eek new chapter!) text & thinks instead about sex [*what we
designate by* below *and* behind, eh] then about *about* it's true
ey are not thinking sex but around it ey are not thinking T
but around them ugh artspeak cliché negative space ey refuse
it there must be some other way: not *over* or *about* fuck prepositions & pronouns & particles parts   apart   ed)
um all this risk of being in *or even thinking* about, *and* –
Yeah I best jet get back to campus before (*I'm not over*)

& M walks home thinking   lids   something ey've never made
                sees   them   hanging
canopic jartops with zoomorphic   the corbel stone
that sits   titfers (*eir favourite piece of landlady
slang   back when ey first lived in the East End*   back
whenfucktwentyyearsago   before *T*)   top hat
sat on eir snakesbowler   bowled (back [back!]
to [to!]) *over*   oh   sits (or is it trips)
hard into a bench as traffic   avoids the ULEZ
used to make them giggle   well that beats
crying into a cocked ~ (whatever that is) pull it down
over one eye   & if this is   (what) mourning   over
(is like)   then I need
                    (someone)

                              to (not) put   a lid on it

3   Sir Graves C. Haughton, *A Short Inquiry Into the Nature of Language
With a View to Ascertain the Original Meanings of Sanskrit Pronouns Eluci-
dated by Comparison With the Greek and Latin*, 7.

Resources

If you suspect you or someone you know is in an abusive relationship, romantic or otherwise, please reach out to someone you trust. Here are some resources that you might find helpful. If your internet activity is being monitored, you can use a library's PCs or icognito mode on your computer or have a friend be in touch for you.

WOMEN'S AID (England) provide life-saving services including housing for women and children. On their website they have a useful workbook to figure out the best way to get out of your current situation.
Website: https://www.womensaid.org.uk
Helpline: 0808 2000 247 (run with Refuge)

REFUGE
Email: helpline@refuge.org.uk
Helpline: 0808 2000 247

MEN'S ADVICE LINE provides confidential help for all men experiencing domestic violence.
Email: info@mensadviceline.org.uk
Helpline: 0808 801 0327 (Mon to Fri: 9 AM to 5 PM)

ASHIANA SHEFFIELD aims to help black, Asian, minority ethnic and refugee women in England, Wales and Scotland as a result of domestic abuse and forced marriage and 'honour'-based violence. Also supports children and young people.
Helpline: 0114 255 5740
info@ashianasheffield.org.uk
ashianasheffield.org

RESPECT NOT FEAR is a website for young people about domestic violence.
respectnotfear.co.uk

THE HIDE OUT is a Women's Aid website to help young people understand domestic abuse, and how to take positive action if it's happening to them.
thehideout.org.uk

THE FORCED MARRIAGE UNIT is a joint initiative between the Foreign Office and Home Office. It assists actual and potential victims of forced marriage, as well as professionals working in the social, educational and health sectors. It is illegal in the UK to force or coerce someone into marriage.
020 7008 0151
fmu@fco.gov.uk
gov.uk/forced-marriage

HAVOCA (Help for Adult Victims of Child Abuse) provides information to any adult who is suffering from past childhood abuse. Website includes survivors' forum.
havoca.org

LIFECENTRE provides telephone counselling for survivors of sexual abuse and those supporting survivors. Also offers face-to-face counselling and art therapy groups in West Sussex.
PO Box 58, Chichester PO19 8UD
Freephone helpline: 0808 802 0808
Text helpline: 07717 989 022
lifecentre.uk.com

ONE IN FOUR is an advocacy service, counselling service (available over skype and in several languages) and information for people who have experienced sexual abuse.
oneinfour.org.uk

THE SURVIVORS TRUST is a UK network of support organisations for survivors of rape, sexual violence and childhood sexual abuse. Offers extensive information resources plus details of your local specialist support. thesurvivorstrust.org

RAPE CRISIS (England and Wales) lists local organisations throughout England and Wales with contact details, services offered and opening times. Services are available to women who have been sexually abused at any time in their lives.

National Freephone helpline: 0808 802 9999 (12–12.30 pm, 7pm–9.30pm every day, plus 3pm–5.30pm weekdays)

info@rapecrisis.org.uk

rapecrisis.org.uk

MANKIND provides one-to-one counselling, therapeutic groups and couple counselling to men (age 18+) who have experienced sexual abuse at any time in their lives.

tel: 01273 911 680

admin@mankindcounselling.org.uk

mankindcounselling.org.uk

SURVIVORS UK gives support for men who have been raped or sexually abused. Also provides webchat, face-to-face counselling and support groups in the London area.

020 3598 3898

help@survivorsuk.org

survivorsuk.org

Opening hours: Mon to Fri: 10.30am to 9pm, Sat to Sun: 10am to 6pm.

MOSAC is a voluntary organisation supporting non-abusing parents and carers whose children have been sexually abused, providing support, advice, information and counselling following the discovery of sexual abuse.
helpline: 0800 980 1958
enquiries@mosac.org.uk
mosac.org.uk

THE LUCY FAITHFULL FOUNDATION
offers a range of services for individuals and families looking for help, advice, support and intervention with regard to issues surrounding child sexual abuse.
lucyfaithfull.org.uk

STOP IT NOW!
is a confidential freephone helpline for people struggling with sexual thoughts and behaviours towards children. Also supports anyone with a concern, including the parents and carers of children and young people with worrying sexual behaviour, and friends and family worried about the behaviour of another adult.
helpline: 0808 1000 900 (Mon to Thurs: 9am to 9pm; Fri: 9am to 7pm)
email support (confidential): help@stopitnow.org.uk
stopitnow.org.uk

AUTHOR BIOS

Lauren Vevers

Lauren Vevers is a writer from and based in Newcastle upon Tyne. She writes poetry and creative non-fiction about memory, desire and loss. She runs creative writing workshops with youth and community groups in the North. She tweets at @LaurenVevers. http://www.laurenvevers.com

Melissa Gitari

Melissa Gitari works in children's publishing as an editorial assistant. She tweets @mellie_gee.

Rebecca Liu

Rebecca Liu writes essays and criticism on arts, politics, and pop culture. Her work has appeared in the *Times Literary Supplement*, the *Guardian*, and the *Financial Times*. She lives in London by way of Chicago and Hong Kong. She is a staff writer at *Another Gaze* and a digital assistant at *Prospect Magazine*. @becbecliuliu

Susannah Dickey

Susannah Dickey is the author of two poetry pamphlets, I had some very slight concerns (2017) and genuine human values (2018), both published by *The Lifeboat*, Belfast. Her poetry has appeared in *The White Review*, *Magma* and *Ambit*, and she was shortlisted for *The White Review* short story prize in 2018. Her first novel, *Tennis Lessons*, will be published in 2020 by Doubleday. @SusannahDickey

Vanessa Pelz-Sharpe

Vanessa Pelz-Sharpe is a writer, born and bred in London. Working primarily within the creative non-fiction genre, she focuses on issues such as queer sexuality, chronic illness, Kim Kardashian, and millennial poverty. @sarcastathon

Tori Truslow

Tori Truslow lives, writes, collaborates and schemes in London. Their writing has appeared most recently Sidekick Books' interactive bat-based anthology Battalion, and has been shortlisted for the British Science Fiction Association Award. With Claire Trévien they co-run Verse Kraken, a series of adventurous creative writing retreats. They currently work for the charity Arts Emergency, and are helping develop a new advocacy project for disabled creative workers. @toritruslow

Zahrah Nesbitt-Ahmed

Zahrah Nesbitt-Ahmed is a Gender & Development Specialist, currently living and working in Florence, Italy. She is also the founder of the African literary blog, bookshy.

Marian Sloane

Marian Sloane is a children's Illustrator and comic artist currently based in Wales.

Maz Hedgehog

Maz Hedgehog is a spoken word poet who loves to reimagine folklore and mythologies. She's performed at events across the North West of England and beyond. Her debut chapbook, *Vivat Regina* was published by Superbia Books in partnership with Manchester Pride.

Lexi Earl

Lexi Earl is a writer and science communicator. For her day job she translates complex research findings into ordinary prose so that regular people can understand just what scientists get up to in their labs. The rest of her time is spent writing about food, mental health, and defining a successful life outside of work. She is the author of *Schools and Food Education in the 21st century* (Routledge, 2018) and is working on a book on school gardens. She blogs at: lexislettuces.blog

Mikael Johani

Mikael Johani is a poet and translator in Jakarta, Indonesia. He juggles between being an Oulipoet and a house husband.

Anya Rompas

Anya Rompas has written two collections of poetry, "Kota Ini Kembang Api" and "Non-Spesifik", both published by Gramedia Pustaka Utama in Indonesia. Her collection of personal essays, "Familiar Messes and Other Essays", was published by Kepustakaan Populer Gramedia. She co-founded Komunitas BungaMatahari in 2000, one of the first online poetry communities in Indonesia, famous for its motto "Semua bisa berpuisi" ("Poetry for all"). She is one of the organisers of Paviliun Puisi, a monthly poetry open mic in Jakarta.

Kasim Mohammed

Kasim Mohammed is an Assistant Editor at Penguin Random House. He was longlisted for the 4th Estate B4ME Short Story Prize and shortlisted for Hachette's Mo Siewcherran Prize. He has had a short story published in *The Good Journal*, and is represented by Juliet Pickering at Blake Friedmann. He is currently working on his first novel.

Jen Calleja

Jen Calleja has published personal essays in Somesuch Stories and PEN Transmissions, and has a long-form essay forthcoming from Rough Trade Books on goblins and punk. Her collections of poetry and prose are *Serious Justice* (Test Centre, 2016), *Hamburger in the Archive* (if a Leaf Falls, 2019) and *I'm Afraid That's All We've Got Time For* (Prototype, 2020). She was shortlisted for the Man Booker International Prize 2019 for her translation of Marion Poschmann's *The Pine Islands* (Serpent's Tail). She is also a senior trainer for the Good Night Out Campaign.

Isha Karki

Isha Karki's short fiction has appeared in *Lightspeed Magazine*, *Mslexia* and *The Good Journal*. She is a Clarion West graduate and winner of the 2019 London Writers Awards. @ishakarki11

Kate Young

Kate Young is an award-winning food writer and cook. The Little Library Café, a collection of recipes inspired by her favourite books, was named Blog of the Year in 2017 by the Guild of Food Writers. Her first book, *The Little Library Cookbook*, was shortlisted for the Fortnum & Mason's debut food book award and won a World Gourmand food writing award. Kate writes about food and books for various publications in the UK, and is currently working on her second cookbook. She lives in the English countryside. @bakingfiction

Anna Kahn

Anna Kahn is a Barbican Young Poet and a London Library Emerging Writer. She has gigged a lot. Her work has been published in journals (*The Rialto*, *The London Magazine*) and anthologies (*Why Poetry: The Lunar Poetry Podcasts Anthology*, *The Dizziness of Freedom*.)

So Mayer

So Mayer is a writer, bookseller and activist. Recent publications include *Tender Questions* (with Preti Taneja, Peninsula, 2018) and *jacked a kaddish* (Litmus, 2018), as well as contributions to *Not That Bad* (Allen & Unwin, 2018), *At the Pond* (Daunt, 2019), and *She Found it At the Movies* (Red Press, 2020); other Medusa poems have recently appeared in Trans Love (JKP, 2019), The White Review 25, a) glimpse) of) 4, and on Visual Verse.

This book would not have been possible without the support from our friends and family, the hard work of our contributors and the generous pledges via Kickstarter and pre-orders from our website.

Creating a book is a team effort, and 3 of Cups Press would like to thank everyone who helped bring *On Relationships* from disparate pieces to a published book.

Clare Bogen
Lizzie Huxley-Jones
Laura Jones
Molly Llewellyn
Sara Magness
Vanessa Peterson
C.F. Prior
Fran Roberts